THE STINGING FLY

Issue 36 Volume Two | Summer 2017

'… God has specially appointed me to this city, so as though it were a large thoroughbred horse which because of its great size is inclined to be lazy and needs the stimulation of some stinging fly…'

—Plato, *The Last Days of Socrates*

The Stinging Fly
new writers, new writing
PO Box 6016, Dublin 1
stingingfly@gmail.com

Publisher/Editor
Declan Meade

Poetry Editor
Eabhan Ní Shúileabháin

Design & Layout
Fergal Condon

Assistant Editor
Fiona Boyd

Eagarthóir Filíochta
Aifric MacAodha

Website
Ian Maleney

Contributing Editors
Emily Firetog, Dave Lordan, Thomas Morris & Sean O'Reilly

Printed by Walsh Colour Print, County Kerry

ISBN 978-1-906539-62-7   ISSN 1393-5690

The Stinging Fly gratefully acknowledges the support of The Arts Council /
An Chomhairle Ealaíon.

NEW POEMS

The Stinging Fly was established in 1997 to publish and promote the best new Irish and international writing.

Now published twice a year (April and October), we welcome open submissions on a regular basis.

Please read the submission guidelines on our website.

Keep in touch: sign up to our e-mail newsletter, become a fan on Facebook, or follow us on Twitter for regular updates about our publications, workshops and events.

stingingfly.org | facebook.com/StingingFly | @stingingfly

Rorschach Test

I happened to be in the city just after the line through it had been rubbed out. It had cut deep and the imprint was still strong. Faces, voices, stories accrued to the memory of the wound.

There were backstreets full of motor workshops, windows fuddled with car parts. A confectionery of little churches. In the pottery district, brushes licked bowls so lightly the marks meant birds' wings.

North and south had been closed to each other since the sixties. Later, certain classes of tourist were allowed to cross. Now at last the citizens themselves could experience or revisit the other half of their city.

To make the crossing, you had to walk a long, earthen corridor with low clusters of buildings at either end. Cue a pageantry of uniforms and documents. There were strict controls on timing; the corridor was open only between such-and-such o'clock, and each side had different rules about how long you could spend in the other half without being penalised. The new freedom was like a package of knives, elaborately wrapped.

The north was visibly poorer than the south. The food was spicier, the vendors friendlier and the siesta was more universally observed so that, when I got there, the streets were eerie in the afternoon heat. Huge banners hung on the facades of buildings: pictures of the Founder on a white background, with legends that might have been threats or promises.

I chose a small, shaded restaurant for lunch and soon got talking to the only other diner there. His English was very good. He was from the other side but hadn't been able to travel these streets since he was a twelve-year-old boy, when he used to cycle through them on his way to school.

I imagined him hurtling along, whistling, barely sparing a glance. At twelve you have so many other preoccupations, and how could you know that streets were about to be snatched from you. In the long afterwards he must have closed his eyes and tried to summon every door, every stone.

Now he was crossing daily to eat lunch there. The language was coming back to him—he had heard it spoken a lot in his youth and he enjoyed practising what he knew. It amazed him that, although he remembered so many words, he had forgotten how good the food was.

The following day, back in the south, I was drinking coffee at a crowded café on the edge of a square. A news team was at work there, quizzing passers-by on how they felt about the newly unfolded city.

I heard a grunt and turned to see a man whose face shone with insult. They should ask me, he said. I could tell them. I would say why should I show my passport in my own country? To cross my own city? To be told what time to come and go at? And for this I am expected to jump up and down and clap! He banged his glass down on the table.

If you cut a city in half, can you solder it back together again? One blot says of course, and smiles, talks, eats, and makes a shape like the sun rising out of the sea. One blot says fuck you, you can shove your controls, I will never relent, I will never forget. He makes a shape like blood seeping out from under a door.

What do you see?

Katherine Duffy

Safe in a Box

Jill Crawford

Your girl comes to check on your oul boy afternoons, after her domestic shift at the clinic.

Did yez never think of havin a wee un ever, Sam?

Aye, we'd one that died, he says. Never left hospital. Brain-sick so it was.

Sorry to hear that, your girl says.

Augh, it was a long, long while ago, sixty-five odd years. But I did wonder why the Lord would do that till us.

Aye, your girl says, I'm sure ye did.

He's terrible frail got, fading ears, drowning eyes, hands murky—death's nibbling at the chapped, puffed, crooked tips of him. Still he likes a chat so he does, and as they're gabbling, your girl mentions she's wife of a man, who was son of a man, who was son of a woman who used to own The Flax Inn, there in the town.

Your oul boy once worked for that woman who owned The Flax Inn, back when he had subtle eyes and supple fingers, and was a carpenter by trade.

Aye, I 'member, he says. Heck of a business woman, hi. She missed nothin. So she'd have been yer grandmammy-in-law. What was it now she went by? Murphy. But here, ye're not Murphy?

Naw, my fella's Murphy. I'm Brennan, your girl says. Didn't change my name when I married.

That right?

Aye, didn't feel right in the end. Tried it, but didn't feel right. My wee uns are Murphy, but ye know, I couldn't make peace with it. Ye were given yer daddy's name an' ye'll stick with it, I said to meself. An' sure, his ma's still about, so there's a Mrs Murphy already. So I'm just Brennan.

Well there ye are, your oul boy says.

Didn't go down at all well, I don't mind tellin ye.

Sure it takes all sorts.

Davey's ma didn't speak to me for a fortnight.

Boy's a dear! Ye're just right, I reckon, cos it's yer name an' ye've to answer till it.

Your oul boy thinks for a bit—Maud Murphy, he says. I built her a kitchen once. Her wee son picked up a dinted chisel an' scraped his self, an' the mother gave the child a clout for touchin what he wasn't s'posed to touch, so the wee fella got a double punishment really.

Sure he's dead now so he is, your girl says.

Augh, is that right, is it? I 'member him like yesterday. The tar-black hair of him an' the wee scraped knees.

I never even met him for Davey an' me had just started courtin, an' he hadn't showed me till his folks yet. Aye, Mickey's been gone these years.

Never heard tell of that one, oul boy says, wondering now why he's still here when that child's already been a man and gone; bit of fun though, piecing the puzzle with your girl who comes. Would ye like to come to Polepatrick with me t'morra? he says. Company, like?

Oul boy used to drive to the cemetery every day, sometimes twice, to talk to his dead one and tend the flowers and have a wee gossip with a nice throughother critter named Angela.

Angela's an angel for stray felines, he chuckles. Ach now, she's right an' dacent so she is, if a mite strange, an' she'd never see a beast starve so I wouldn't say a cursed word about her. But sure, I haven't clapped eyes on my pal Angela since they ripped my car off of me.

That's a dreadful pity, your girl says. I'd not see ye stuck. I'll be fit to drive ye down if I can get Davey's ma to mind the wee uns that wee bit longer t'morra, but ye know, she's terrible particular about the notice even though she hasn't a body at home anymore. In fact, I best be makin a move or the same one will be complainin. I'll see ye t'morra then, Sam?

Aye, it'll be awful nice to get a dander an' a jabber, an' not be bottled up all day.

He hoists himself from his chair, dainty-like, mouldy-jointed. The rickety coop of the ribs swivels left and right in seek of something, and he hobbles over to his stick that's propped against the rim of the fireplace—a wavery limb of blackthorn with a knob at one end he once pulled out of a ghoulish hedgerow when the sap was down and his fingers were fit to polish the good elegant length of it. Stick and he follow her into the hall. His spare hand, mesh of knuckle and vein sealed in scaly mottled skin, fumbles along the wall for balance.

It's our seventieth anniversary in a week, he says, shuffling slippers across the carpet. Nine years since she left me here on my own.

Tears come, for himself maybe. He wipes them away with the heel of his palm. At the coat stand, he delves a paw into the pocket of an anorak and rummages.

I'll be seein ye then, Sam, your girl says loudly, making for the door before he finds what he's after. Ye've got a nice dinner to beat into ye later. Don't forget to take the clingy film off this time before ye nuke it.

Agh, ye're awful good, he says, grinning. Ye're awful good to an oul boy, ye girl ye.

He squeezes her hand with cool, darkening fingers, placing a note in her palm.

Now Sam, she says, I'm only after tellin ye a million times that I don't want yer money. I'm glad to help. I toul' ye that.

He tuts and shakes his head. Get on away on with ye. Ye never accept, an' sure it's nothin. Times are tight. Ye can buy the youngsters a treat with it. An' maybe ye'll bring them fer a visit one day?

Her hand hovers in the space between her flesh and his, not wanting to return to her till it's empty.

Now listen. I can't be takin this. Ye get a scarce enough pension, no doubt.

Well, I don't drink an' I don't smoke an' I don't drive an' my dog's gone, so who am I goin te give it till anyways? Take it. He pushes her hand to her, eyes fierce—It would please me. An' sure I can't bring it wi' me!

That's ridiculous me takin money off an oul fella, she says, closing the note in her fist. Thank you, Sam. An' there's to be no more giftin of tenners, alright? I do fer ye cos I want to, an' that'll be the end of it.

He stands at the open door as she crosses the road, gets into her car and clicks key in ignition. He minds those tremors under him, cute rumble of the engine, grind of his boot on the clutch to clinch power, and propulsion. He totters back inside and looks out through the patterned glass of the shut front door. Winding her windy down, she waves over, brief streak back and forth like a rag in a puff of wind.

She flicks on the radio. O-O-Ophelia, The Lumineers. As she drives away, she toots thrice at the blur of him, thinking he might not be able to hear too clear from all the way in there, but he can still hear right enough sometimes.

Her car slants into the pitted lane a good quarter of an hour late. When it finds the farmhouse, Davey's ma is ready and waiting outside the back door with a face like an angry cat and the wee uns already in their coats, baby girl on one hip while the boy toes a stone with his welly boot and chases after. There's a gap between boy and baby girl, gap enough for three other wee uns your girl wasn't fit to bring to the world whole.

Davey's ma carried eleven sound children of which Davey's last and most treasured, and the one whose name, at age eighteen, was put on the mortgage of his folks' new farmhouse, so his own young family hadn't a hope of getting a mortgage to raise a dwelling place of their own, in spite of all this land about them.

I'll not ask ye in for a cup of tay, his ma says. I've a wil' pile of cleanin up to do what with my floor-layers in an' out. An' time's marchin.

Aye well, I'm late cos I had to pop in an' get a few things at the supermarket for their dinners, an' for his piece t'morra, your girl says.

He'd get given a quare an' tasty beef stew the night if he were in my house, his ma says.

Aye, well he'll be no worse off with me. Anyway, he's lambin tonight straight after the brickie work. He'll eat on the hoof or when he's done, your girl says.

There's a triple-pack of frozen Chicken Kiev that was on offer at Iceland, sweating in the boot of her car.

Ye'll be wantin yer milk with ye, his ma says and plods back into her flashy cavern that sprang from the grave of the plain, small farmhouse, where Davey and his ten brothers and sisters were reared.

Here wee man, your girl says, sweeping her boy up in her arms. Where's my big kiss then?

Hi mammy. I saw an orange tractor today, he says, squirming out of her grasp, off and after his stone that's angular and lopsided, travelling slantways across the broken tarmac instead of rolling directly.

His ma comes back with baby girl in one arm, squat bottle of lemony milk in the other and a plastic bag dangling from her wrist, clinking quietly with dirty vacant bottles.

Did she not feed much then? your girl says. I thought she'd sup the lot.

Well look, I tried to get it into her, but I'm not a miracle-worker. She's a picky wee skitter with a powerful scant hunger.

Your girl says nothing, takes her daughter, sets her into the car seat, belts her up briskly. The quizzical eyes catch hers and she cups the crest of the round, fair head with her hand. Are ye happy to have yer mammy back? she says, muddling a cluster of buttery strands. Ye've the eyes of yer dear dead granda, my wee pet.

The child's face that was full of thought cracks open and cackles in raspy spurts that ripple across the fields and startle the beasts at their grazing.

That's a devilish laugh for a wee girl, his ma says.

Your girl says nothing but looks over, hard. She's always at the wee girl, always favouring the boy. Classic farmer's wife. Unless it's because of the lost ones.

The boy hops up into his car seat, ready to be clipped in. Come on, mammy, he says. Come on, come on! Just do it, will ye? Let's go.

Give me a minute, will ye? Your girl's pulling the straps tight on the baby seat while Davey's ma just stands at the threshold of her precious house with her arms the one length and no thought of giving a hand. Too busy barring the way in.

The boy is flailing arms and legs now, kicking the rear of the seat in front.

Houl' yer horses you, she says, reaching across and handing him her phone. Here! Content yerself with that a wee minute while I speak to yer granny. She hokes out a dummy from the Tupperware box in the changing bag, lodges it in the baby's mouth and turns to his ma—Would ye be able take them for an extra hour t'morra? she says. Cos I've to take the wee oul man to the cemetery on a jaunt to where his wife's buried.

Oh ye do, do ye? An' are ye gettin paid for that?

No, I'm not.

Will he be givin ye back our petrol money then? his ma says. Ye get little enough out of him as it is.

It's volunt'ry, Yvonne. There's no harm in helpin a body for no reason, for once. An' I wouldn't begrudge the wee man a trip up the cemetery. Sure, it's no more than a mile out of town, your girl says.

His ma sniffs. Can't he not take his self?

No, he can't. It's too far for him to walk with his knees, an' his eyes are bad. They took his car off him when he crashed into the side of a house.

Jeepers. Did he now? Well, he's not yers to be worryin about. Haven't ye enough on yer hands with two wee uns an' a workin fella to look after.

He's got nobody, your girl says. He didn't have a squad of youngsters like you had.

Aye, well there's only one bothers with me now—my David. Ye'll no doubt do as ye please, his ma says. Away on with y'uns. She turns into the house, beating the air with her hand in a gesture that's as much a shooing away as a farewell.

Thanks a bunch, your girls says in her head, because she can't speak it aloud without consequences.

Bye granny, the boy hollers, not lifting his face that's mesmerised as he prods at the screen that's thumping tinny music and flickering colours.

Here, what's that yer watchin? your girl says.

Peppa, says the wee boy.

Why are ye watching it in Russian, ye wee weirdo?

The day's fading from the fields as they bounce down the lane and head to the bungalow, ten mile up the dulled road in a cul de sac in the village.

At home, she sees them fed, milked, bedded, and plonks down on the couch for an hour or two of telly before she kips. Davey won't be in till late if he even makes it home and doesn't go to his ma's. She gives a great yawn. Her boobs are sore, hefty. She hokes out the pump, puts the flange of the thing to her tit and starts compressing the dicky lever to suck. An in-an'-an-out, an in-an'-an-out, her eyes on the telly or she gets annoyed by the paltry drip of the stuff. *Louis Theroux: Twilight of the Porn Stars*. She never mulled what happens to them after—

Tommy says, It's not normal to leave somebody you love to go and have sex with somebody you don't love. My heart's home safe in a box where nobody can touch it, and I go out and do what I have to do, and then I come home. But I always get my heart broken.

Louis says, I thought your heart was safe in a box?

Tommy says, Yes, but sometimes I take it out even when I don't mean to.

Your girl says to her telly, Aye well, get used till it. Hearts don't do what they're ast. They plop ye in it before ye know it an' then it's too late.

She unlatches herself and extracts the other one, the slow boob. Yer turn, she says, kneading and jiggling it slightly to agitate the milky glands. Aie, fuck sake! The nipple's stingy. Eyes back to the TV screen—

Alana says, Everyone has problems. Everyone. I went into porn because I wanted to go into porn. It had nothing to do with my dad being incarcerated.

Wee Catherine's folks are porn stars who fell in love, got married and raised her up just fine. She's good at her school and wants to be a police officer. She says, I'd like to stop people from doing the wrong thing, because I want everybody to do the right thing. Her daddy killed his self because he thought he was failing at being a proper man.

After it's over, she switches to the news. Syria. Zika. Europe. Westminster. Stormont. A murder in Lurgan. A young girl dragged through Belfast Crown Court for deciding not to be a mammy yet. A hit and run. A house fire. An' the weather, which is to be a bit shite for a spell.

She puts off the telly and sits in peace until she's done milking.

Can't tolerate listenin to that oul news, she says to the room. Does my head in. Nothin but violent violence an' goings-on that are never good.

A strange car pulls down into the cul de sac, hurling its headlights through the front window. She drops deep in the couch, out of sight, so as not to expose herself. The car turns and leaves, lost likely, but her heart seized for a second there, when those men came to mind who beat the crap out of her fifteen-year-old nephew in his own home, a mile down the road. Drugs, people said, not the RA or anything, cos he was dealing and everybody knowed that. But a body had to wonder if it was cos of something else—like him being bi and brazen about it, thinking it was fine cos of all them uns on the telly. They knocked him into a grim shape with his two legs in plaster, jaw wired. Same week her wee boy was born. The pair of them stuck in the same hospital for different reasons. Still gives her the shivers.

She tosses her contraption in the kitchen sink and puts the half-filled baby bottle in the belly of the fridge, lifting out a part-drunk bottle of white and pouring herself a good sup into a purple plastic glass; everything she has is plastic. Placing the bottle back behind the expressed milk and dilutey juice, she takes her sup into the scullery where she tucks her hair into a Yankees cap and pulls on a grubby dressing gown over her uniform to soak up the stink. Groping in the pocket for her rolling tin, she steps out in her sock soles into the back garden to light up and look at the stars.

Them stars is beautiful, she says to the tip of her cigarette.

Eleven lovely roasts at the back of her throat. She scrapes the butt against the rough wall of the house, drops it into a flower pot, glugs the cold tang down her and goes back in, turning the key behind. Dressing gown and hat go back on the hook of the scullery door. Then she washes her hands and face. All part of the ritual.

Them stars, she says out through the kitchen window, feeling in her their fever for bliss. Her three figurines—*Mammy's ordaments*—sit up on the window sill, out of reach of the wee boy. They are carved out of wood with simple white frocks, bare faces, wire wings. One for each she's lost. Three daughters, is the notion she has. Sleep tight, she says, touching each with a fingertip before she heads bedwards.

After she's peed, she swallows her pill, brushes her teeth and scours the gaps with the fiddly do-fer the dentist gave her because her gums keep bleeding. The body's not just mended yet since she had the wee girl. Troublesome birth, but they're both here.

In bed, she can't settle. She's all hot and bothered. If he were here, but he's never here when she's roused. Her hand reaches down to the squishy nub and taps softly as if she's knocking at the door of an elf. She conjures up that porn star girl on the telly, the one with the springy hair and dark eyes. So different to her. All gilt and pert and smooth, while your girl's all saggy and clotted. She can't wait to get back into her running shoes. At school, she was the best cross-country runner, and that included the boys.

He comes in the middle of the night, too knackered to shower, splashing his face, hands, oxters and bollocks at the bathroom sink, swamping all round him as usual. Then he climbs into bed with a clatter, still smelling of new lamb, and starts poking at her. Poke, poke, poke till she's full woke and he says, Do ye want some?

Might as well get somethin out of this arrangement, she says, but she's too tired to even raise her bones.

He scales down her and sups until she comes. Then he says, Were ye at the drink and the fags? Sniff sniffing at her. The nose he has.

So? she says. Ye said nowt about it when we were courtin so ye can shut up about it now. She's boiling, because he's shamed her though she's done nothing wrong. Ye can please yer fuckin self, she says. Comin in an' stirrin me up at this hour. It's a little power she has these days, what with the wee uns and everything else.

He turns away his craving, bare steep wide back to her, like a rock face she'll never get a grip on.

Why didn't ye just stop at yer ma's, her all alone in that massive house with her fancy fuckin floors while we rot here in this titchy hole with me payin all the bills, an' just barely?

Wisht, woman, he breathes. My ma's had nothin all her life.

Well, she's doin fine now for a farmer's widow.

It's her time, he says. Ye'll get what's comin when she's gone. That'll make ye happy, I s'pose.

Aye, wait till my ma's dead, your girl says. Ye didn't tell me that when ye proposed, did ye?

He says nothing and having blurted it, she feels bad, even if it is the truth. There's no more talk and he's gone when she wakes at half past five, with the wee girl gurning to be fed.

When it's done, she goes into the kitchen for a drink of water. He's left his piece behind to punish her. Two rounds of good cheddar and pickle let to waste on the counter, so he can go to his ma's and get spoilt rotten with a fry-up.

Aye, the smug oul face on ye, your girl says as if his ma were right there, hovering at the door, judging. Ye bitter oul bitch, she says, as though she were able to say all the things she can't say. Well if he won't eat it, I will. She tears open the tin foil and bites a hunk off each corner of each sandwich till her mouth's packed to the hilt. Flecks of bread and cheese drop from her lips onto the lino. The butter slithers across her teeth.

As she's fixing to get the wee uns out the door on time, the phone goes.

Hello, it's me, his ma says.

Aye, I know. I'm comin now, your girl says. I'm on my way. I'm halfway out the door.

Aye, well… his ma says.

Something's brewing. What's up, Yvonne? Her stomach curls.

Well, I'm not feelin at all up till it t'day, his ma says. I think ye'll need to find someone else to look after the wee uns for a change.

What? Well what's wrong with ye? your girl says.

Augh, my pains. His ma groans.

Yer pains?

Aye, my pains in my chest. An' my head. His ma sighs.

Well… Your girl's fingers go to her eyes to muddle them, trying to come up with something. She keeps her voice steady—Well, can ye not take them though for a wee bit, because I have my work to get to within the hour, an' I don't expect I'll find anybody else straight away? I can always call a few friends from the clinic, an' see if they'll pick up the youngsters from ye a bit later?

Naw, I don't think I can take them at all t'day, his ma says. I would take them. Ye know, I never would like to say no to my own grandchildren, but I'm not feelin at all good for it today.

Your girl knows rightly what she's at—Is he there with ye?

Who?

Who d'ye think? Davey. Is he there?

Now why would he be here wi' me?

Was he in earlier for brekkie? your girl says.

Aye, he did land in earlier for a bite.

Aye he did. An' what did he tell ye?

Nothin.

Nothin?

What goes on between husband an' wife is none of mine.

Damn fuckin right it isn't, your girl thinks—An' so he said nothin, an' ye're not goin to help me out t'day?

Now you listen here, madam. I look after yer children regular enough, I reckon.

They're yer son's youngsters too. An' isn't he out farmin for near-enough free to keep ye in new kitchens while I put a roof over our heads an' food in our bellies?

Well, that's just shockin ungracious an' ungrateful, his ma says.

Look Yvonne, if ye don't take the wee uns, I'll have to take off my work, I'll lose the day's wages, an' they'll get pissed off an' cut my shifts for the rest of the month. Just, please. I'm feelin a bit weary, an' I can't be dealin with the mind games fer once.

I toul' ye, daughter. I'm not feelin at all well, an' I can't do it t'day.

Aye, ye mean ye won't, your girl says.

I don't appreciate yer doubtin all I do fer ye, what with me here on my own, an' at my age.

Fine, fuck ye then, she bursts, not able to hold it longer. Yer pity party won't wash with me, so ye may try it out on yer son instead. An' while ye're at it, ye may tell him as well that we'll be eatin baked beans again fer the foreseeable future, an' if we can't make the rent, we'll be movin in with you whether ye like it or not. She hangs up and presses her eyes.

The wee boy's at her other hand, nipping the web of stretchy skin between thumb and forefinger.

Ow that hurts, she says.

Mammy, we forgot to scrub our teef.

Ye're right, she says. We did forget. Thank you for remindin.

She scoops up the baby and follows the wee boy into the bathroom. He holds out his dinosaur brush alongside hers while she squeezes on the toothpaste with her spare hand. As they stand at the mirror brushing, she's thinking—Katrina? Jolene? Debbie? Maybe Denise? Would Mrs Mac be fit to do her a favour? Or what about that friendly girl who doesn't work who lives at the bottom of the estate? What's-her-name. Maybe she'd take them. But naw, isn't she off to Dublin for a ween of days for a pop concert and the shoppin?

A queasy gust flitters through her and she stoops down to set the baby on its back on the brown bathmat where the wee limbs curl up into the air like those air roots on an orchid. Your girl sets herself down on the toilet seat and leans forward to ease the sicky feeling.

Are ye okay, mammy? her boy says.

Aye, she says, Mammy's just got a bit of a runny tummy. Probably got it from you, ye rascal!

Ye'll just have to do a big poo, he says. To get the bad out.

Aye, I will, she says, I will later.

And then she thinks of it. Naw, it's not possible. Sure, the baby's only four month old an' she's on the pill. Naw, that couldn't happen. Sure, they'd settled on two, an' she's happy with her lot. Two mouths are enough with them both workin, an' nobody dependable to childmind, an' her with no folks to help her out, an' all the trouble before with the wee uns that didn't come right. Naw…

Conor, she says, Will ye go into the fridge an' fetch me one of them wee boxes of juice?

The wee boy runs out to the kitchen, all happy to have a job, but the baby's getting grumbly. She tickles the sole of a tiny foot, pushes the step-up stool to one side and reaches to the back of the bathroom cabinet under the sink. Wasn't there a test left over from last time? Jesus H. Christ, she's fucked if she's to go through this again already. It's not here. She can't find it. She threw it out cos she didn't need it any more. No matter, cos the more she thinks of it, the surer she is. She just knows. When ye're a mammy, ye just know.

What the bloody fuck am I going to do? she says.

Ye've to get to yer work, the wee boy says, walking in with a carton of apple juice. Cos if ye don't get till yer work, they'll get pissed off an' cut yer shifts, ye said. He gives it to her with the sealed straw that he's pulled off the outside of the box. Can I've a sup too?

Aye, you go ahead first, pet. Ye want me to prick it for ye?

What's shifts, mammy?

It's the time ye have to spend at yer work.

How many minutes?

Aye, or hours.

Time is like, four years?

Aye, like the age ye're at, Conor. Now I'm puttin yer sister down for a nap in her cot, so will ye go in an' put on the telly for a bit, or do some drawin or somethin? Mammy just has to use the toilet so she does. An' I need five minutes on my own, but I'll leave the door open.

No worries, the wee boy says. D'ye want some before I go?

Naw, ye can have it all, wee man. Drink up, she says.

He trots out with the apple juice carton, stripy straw between his teeth, humming.

She puts the wee girl in the Moses basket to doze and comes back into the bathroom, pushes the door part-closed, steps into the hollow bath and lies down, pulling the bath towel down round her. O she. Violence of this body betrayin her. O just. Takin over all provinces of her. An' again so soon. She just. No time to come back, none for only her, when. O she wanted to feed her own self now, get strong an' good, an' rear the two she has she loves to death. If she were meant to bring more, she'd have brung the others out with a pulse. An' no choice, no choosin. Why's God done this on her? An' she wasn't careless, wasn't. They've hardly done it since the wee girl came. Doesn't that not matter? Is she to deny herself and him and both forever, in case? And if she doesn't want it, worry of them catchin her, a bad unnatural girl all over the telly, prison sentence, criminal record so she can't get jobs or go to Disneyland America. O she wanted to be elastic again an' alone in her own skin, an' out an' about, carryin her own self just cos the last five year she's been carryin others. She's content. Another's too much. She can't do another, sick with worry all the time.

How dare ye? she whispers to the presence, if he's even there an' gives a toss, an' isn't some oul devil. Why've ye snared me in my flesh, when there's no call for that to be so these days? Not made to be a shell for every chick that springs haphazard. Need a break from strainin to bring new children. Want to get back to my own body, own. Want to work with my wee uns I have, an' help with the lambs, an' get at my runnin, an' keep an eye on yer oul boy in his last wee bit. Other things doin. That not count? Done plenty, done enough. No, no, no, can't endure it further. As she rises, the towel crumples in a heap at the base of the dry bath.

She finds her phone in the kitchen, disconnects it from the house wireless connection, goes to Play Store, looks up Best Anonymous Browser, chooses Tor Browser for Android, installs it after she's cleared some pictures of the wee uns from her Gallery to free up space. She downloads Orbot whatever that is, cos that's a must apparently, hoping there's still room in there to home that too. Opening up the new secure browser, she types 'shop safe pills for miscarriage' into a search box.

There are two million, two hundred and forty thousand results.

Annemarie Ní Churreáin is a poet from northwest Donegal. She has been awarded literary fellowships by Akademie Schloss Solitude (Germany), Jack Kerouac House (Orlando) and Hawthornden Castle (Scotland). In 2016, she received a Next Generation Artists Award from the Arts Council. In Autumn 2017, Annemarie's debut collection *BLOODROOT* is being launched by Doire Press.

Penance

for a girl in trouble, 1951

'Shame.'
    Use this word when you speak of love.

A man of cloth will come.
Your new home is among brides.

Deny
the child inside you is the child you dream at night

and when they cut short your hair,
watch the cuts fall

like the soft fur of an animal
held still by threat.

Find a pale rose climbing a wall
and consider yourself

smaller now
than even a thorn.

In your starched uniform, step into a nameless stream.
Feel the coldness between your thighs.

Say aloud:
'In this life I am drowning.'

Wall

'Between all of them they raise, little by little, a wall that will keep out the thing that lies waiting for the tiniest crack of silence to steal through.'
—Rosario Castellanos

First, a wall that contracts me out of my unfurled state. Next, one that divides me from my own kin. It is the same wall I am sitting on when Green aged nine is pulled from the school yard for yelling *dicks and fannies are what make babies*. I thought I could fly I said when asked why I'd hurled myself forward, arms outspread and eyes closed tight to the world. There are the wall boys who want in under your bra with their cold fingers and the wall girls who will teach you how to leave a bite. There is the wall that goes up inside you the first time you're called a *slut*. There is the wall of grinning wet-lipped farmers that gathers around the teenage girls at the local beauty pageant show as you in a borrowed dress are herded into the ring. *Writer*: wrong answer and you lose to the sergeant's daughter. *It should have been you* the barman sighs as he swipes the taps with a dirty cloth. It could have been me but instead I am scored out of ten and told to try again next year. I am sixteen by the time a fire in my chest begins to burn from the inside out. I am seventeen when I learn how to stave myself. I am eighteen the summer I join my brothers in the building trade, laying concrete, smoothing lines of dark, wet cement. I am standing on the site early one morning with the hot sun in my eyes and a brick in my hand when a man dares to ask me: *what do you know about walls?*

On Visiting Ellis Island

for Mary Thaidhg

I

Maiden. Unskilled. Alone.
The language I find you in is not the one you spoke,

you who taught me that to make a home is to make a sound
in the world, and be understood

> for the bright, black bogs we were raised on,
> heather-furred and spinning invisible gnats
> high into the evening.

What is more vowel than a piece of turf drying in the sun?

II

By night the ferry departs Ellis Island.

In the waves, the stern leaves   a dark kaleidoscope
of lace and disappearing knots.

But I do not think of you as servant in a high collar, long hem.

I think of you as bed-dressed and holding me
against a dream, mothering me back towards the bone
again.

III

In these divided states, I dream you   at the end of your life,

in the peach room with the peach blinds,

upright in a hard-backed chair

        like an ivy that won't take hold
        like a woman mugged of her own name
        like an empty boat

all day tapping the table-tray, having lost your tongue,
        having realised that to lose a home is to wake somewhere
on the ocean
        knowing no cut of earth
           and without a spade for the darkness.

Newborn 1984

for a Dublin mother

The first wrong thing
was this: an extra finger,
boneless and pointless.
The junior doctor said
as he looped a thread
around the infant part
and made a knot, *wait*
for the lot to fall away.

That was the season
Mary Manning refused
to pass an orange through
the checkout
at a Dunnes Stores desk.
A strike was declared,
apartheid made the news:
our battle is nothing
compared to theirs.

And all that summer
an unexpected heat
curled, like a bindweed
root around the city,
bulging and pulsing,
until even the swans
in the charcoal canal
appeared to be posing
the question—
when will it ever end?

In stores, the till drawers
lay open, oranges
sprouted fur
and Mary marched
down O'Connell Street
protesting the divide
of skin from skin
and bone as any less
than bone
as quietly,
beside a cot,
a new mother
still waiting
wept.

The Kerry Foot

at Cahir Saidhbhín*

It began with a foot,
thrown up out of the underworld,
as ceremonious
as a stone,
one morning on the shore
of Fort Saidhbhín, 1984.

This was a warning foot,
a foot of other parts to come;

a foot before fifteen-year-old Ann
died in the grotto giving birth;
a foot before Joanne
circled on a map
for the court
each bog lane
in which an act had occurred;
a foot before the broadcast on RTÉ
of statues weeping blood.

This was the fortune foot of Saidhbhín,
who set a hoof
into the centre of a soldier's fort
to win her human body back.
One touch of the earth
and the hide fell
from her bones.

This foot marked the sand
where soon the air was about to become
animal again.

And as the air hissing salt
rose on its hinds
against the bay,
the Kerry Foot without a name
was placed into an unmarked grave.
Already the body had been claimed
and grieved enough.

---

* 'Cahir Saidhbhín' translates from Irish as 'Fort of Little Sadhbh'. In Irish legend, Saidhbhín was the mother of Oisín. She appears in stories both in human and deer form.

In 1984, 'The Kerry Babies' story unfolded in Cahir Saidhbhín, County Kerry.

A few months before 'The Kerry Babies' story broke, it was reported that a single human foot was found washed up on a shore at Cahir Saidhbhín.

I believe in the universe

Jo Holmwood

There is nothing remarkable about the fact that Ciara is late. When they agreed on half past ten, Brendan supposed that she would arrive closer to twelve, not because she was any less punctual than the rest of them, but because in Leitrim you just added an hour or so to the agreed time.

In the end, she arrives at eleven forty just as Brendan is lighting another fag, and has a fresh pot of coffee bubbling on the electric plate.

'Feck's sake, I thought you were never coming,' he says, not out of genuine frustration but because that is what you are meant to say. And Ciara runs her hands through her hair.

'I know!' she says, as though Leitrim's hold on her is hard to suffer, and no other explanation is necessary. 'Here give us a drag of that, will you?'

They sit for twenty minutes smoking and drinking coffee, before Ciara decides it's time to hit the road.

'The car's a bit full,' she says, as they are stepping out on to the main street. Brendan catches sight of the boxes stuffed in at all angles and mountains of loose paraphernalia.

'Jesus!' he says, pulling the front door closed with a bang.

Ciara lets the handbrake off and the car rolls gently forward. When they are at the top of the hill, she checks her mirror and steers out, knocking it into second and letting it gather momentum before taking her foot off the clutch.

'Don't you think it's time to get a new car?' Brendan says.

'Can't afford it.'

'A new gearbox then?'

'Sure may as well get a new car with the amount that would cost.'

'Hmmm.'

'Anyway, as long as it's always parked on a hill, it's grand.'

'Are there many hills in Galway?'

'Or we can gather a few lads… push it a bit to get it going.'

'Last time we did that it rained.'

'Yeah, that was funny.'

'I don't remember laughing.'

Brendan winds down the window, which is tight and moves with a squeal. There is a tiny edging of moss along the rubber seals that the pane of glass rises out of. He lights a cigarette and holds it by the gap. The sky is a dirty colour, like mashed offal. It throws an erratic spittle over the windscreen, which is not enough for the wipers to clear without leaving smudges. In spite of the rain, Ciara squints in the uncertain glare.

'Pass out me sunnies, will ya?' she says pointing at the glove box. Brendan pulls out a pair of white-framed heart-shaped glasses.

'Those are so gay,' he says.

They are out on the coast road with the radio on. Ciara drives with a certain caution, but doesn't hang about either. Brendan would love to sleep, since he was up into the early hours smoking weed, but he knows it's not cool to leave Ciara devoid of company for the trip.

'How come she's got so much stuff anyways?' He says, jabbing a finger in the direction of the boot, where Helen's things are coiled and stuffed and twisted and shoved.

'I dunno. I guess she likes collecting things.'

'A kleptomaniac.'

'That's stealing.'

'Oh. I thought it was hoarding.'

'No.'

He stares past Ciara at the sea, which can be glimpsed in flashes as they head towards Sligo. The water is dishwater grey. Disappointing, he thinks, since they're on a road trip and you always want to be dazzled on a road trip.

'It's like necrophilia,' he says.

'What is?' asks Ciara, frowning.

'I always mix it up with narcolepsy. Keep thinking it's that falling-asleep thing.'

Ciara laughs, a four-stage rising sequence: Ah-he-he-he.

'There's a bit of a feckin difference,' she says.

'Yeah. I know,' says Brendan, wistfully. 'You could get into some trouble with that.'

Out past Collooney, they take a right at the second roundabout, which no one can ever remember the name of, and onto the N17.

'I wish I was on the EN-SEVENTEEN… stone walls and the grass is green!'

They bellow out two lines before realising they don't know the rest of the words and letting the song trail into a rambling murmur and then a windless hum. Ciara leans forward; rallies herself for the next tranche of the journey, which will seem long and will involve countless dips in velocity as they lag behind auld lads with straw bales in the boot, trailing twine, who Brendan will verbally assault and call 'culchie cunts' even though he is one himself; or Cork registrations with all the heads inside facing left and right, looking for a turning or some landmark in the expansive boggy void; or livestock trucks which Ciara will whine at as she passes them out, staring at the poor bovine bulk, their sorry fate turning her maudlin.

'The world is cruel,' Brendan will say unhelpfully, as if that's all there is to it. 'It's dog eat dog.'

'And you know all about the world!'

'I know enough. I know that we're never gonna change it. So suck it up.'

Halfway to Tubbercurry, they see the sun. It doesn't come out so much as drill through little cracks in the cloud and fire darts of light at any windows and metal surfaces that populate the roadside. They can smell the heavy steam that rises instantly from the damp bog. Ciara breathes deeply with satisfaction.

'I love the smell of the bog,' she says.

'Same as that. We used to go stacking the turf in Clare when I was a kid,' Brendan says. 'Nothing like it. And the tea in the flask. Why does it always taste better from a flask?'

'Dunno. Maybe cause it was steeping. Maybe you were just thirstier.'

A moment of silence.

'Speaking of thirst,' Brendan says.

'No way!' Ciara changes gear. 'We're not stopping.'

But at the other side of Tubbercurry they spot a hitcher, a young lad with a baseball cap and a rucksack hoisted high on one shoulder. He smiles hopefully, his thumb waggling with enthusiasm. He looks happy. He looks young.

'What'll I do?' says Ciara.

'Give the poor fella a lift,' says Brendan. 'There's a good dip in the road here to get off again.'

'But the back is full of stuff.'

'We'll make some space.'

Ciara pulls over.

Brendan twists around, reaches to open the back door, re-angles a pot plant and a long-base lamp, shoves a couple of boxes into the footwell behind Ciara's seat.

'Hello,' says the lad, gamely clambering in, legs bending under him as he settles in the hole Brendan has opened up in the middle. He looms between them, leaning forward.

'Hi.' Ciara smiles. 'Where are you headed?'

'Uh, Galway?' he says. He pronounces the 'a' as in 'salad'.

'G-a-lway, Ciara,' Brendan says, facetiously. 'That's where we're going!'

'No way!'

The lad is clearly European, and has learned from an American teacher.

'Where do you hail from yourself?'

'What? Where I'm from?'

'Yeah.'

'Switzerland.'

'Cool,' says Ciara.

'I'm just travelling. *Shooting the breeze.*'

'Good for you.'

'You've got the lingo.'

'He sure has, Brendan.'

'He's got it down pat.'

'You've got it down pat,' Ciara says, feeling playful.

The lad looks inquisitive, still smiling.

'Don't worry about it. It's a stupid saying.'

'A saying?'

'Yeah, like *shooting the breeze.*'

'Ah.'

Silence. He is processing.

She has been crawling, sliding down the hill on the hard shoulder. She pulls out. A lorry cab with no container beeps its horn. It blares over them. The Swiss boy cowers momentarily. It speeds around them with another little blast.

'Christ!' says Brendan. 'Feckin watch it.'

'Sorry. I was distracted.'

A pause. Ciara winks at Brendan.

'Far too young for you,' Brendan says.

'Still cute though. God love him.'

The lad leans forward between them.

'It was loud. That claxon.'

Brendan laughs, and enjoys the sound of his own laughter. He howls.

'It's funny?'

'It's a horn,' Ciara says.

'Horn?'

'Horn.'

Brendan wipes the tears from his eyes.

'It wasn't that funny,' Ciara says.

Brendan giggles again.

'He's breaking his shite laughing,' she says over her shoulder.

'What? Shite?'

Brendan goes again, his head between his knees, '*A-ha-ha-ha-ha…*'

At the petrol station, they introduce themselves properly. Brendan proffers an awkward hand and shakes the boy's formally. The boy's name is Ralph and Brendan tries it a few times, dutifully attempting the correct pronunciation of the soft 'r' which is an open-mouthed glottal rasp that seems to emanate from the back of the throat, rather than the goofy Anglo front-of-palette pout. Then he offers Ralph a cigarette and they smoke while Ciara seeks out a toilet. When she comes back, she looks at the lad carefully and smiles. He is tall and thin, with a neat squared jaw and fine cheekbones. Effeminate almost.

'How old are you?' she asks.

'Twenty,' Ralph replies with a shrug, as if to say, *who cares*?

'Holy fuck,' says Brendan, genuinely stunned by the extreme youth, and the energy and character required for such journeying. He himself has never exhibited such purpose, although he did spend six months in Amsterdam in his early thirties. *Purpose* couldn't exactly be credited as the driving force of that adventure. Now, Brendan does not consider the future or think of it in good terms or bad. He knows there are days spent with friends that can be chalked up as *good ones*, and days that fall into a drain of ennui and hopelessness which are best forgotten as soon as have they ended. Ciara is a little younger than him, a little more excited by the world in general, but she has suffered knocks too, and shares the same debilitating fear to hope for things that must be striven for, or to follow ambitions that might be eternally doomed to fail.

'Good on you,' is all Brendan can think to say.

They watch the same lorry driver who beeped them on the road emerge from the petrol station and step up into his cab. He takes a swig of his coffee and sets it somewhere on his dashboard, unwraps a breakfast bap from an endless roll of paper and sticks one side of it in his mouth. He starts the engine and steers one-handed from the forecourt.

'Asshole,' Brendan says.

Ralph laughs. 'He is a dick, no?'

Brendan and Ciara exchange an amused glance.

'A gobshite,' Ciara says.

'Total cunt,' Brendan says, slowly, in an instructive manner, hoping the Swiss will copy.

'Jesus, that's awful language altogether,' Ciara says.

'In fairness, you did pull out in front of him,' Brendan says.

'I know.'

They bundle back into the car, Ralph in the back as before. His head sits neatly into the shade of Helen's lamp and the others laugh.

'Will you be all right back there?' Ciara asks.

'I'm grand,' he says.

They laugh.

'*Grand*! Where d'you pick that up?'

'What?'

'Never mind.'

Brendan has his door open and one foot out on the tarmac. He puts a shoulder to the frame of the door and heaves the car forward. Ciara has parked facing the back where the yard dips just slightly into a workshop and car wash. They get enough momentum to rumble into second gear with just enough room to steer round before hitting the wall on the far side.

Ralph says nothing.

They pass Knock, first the airport and then the signs to the holy shrine.

'Want to stop and say a few *Hail Marys*?' Brendan asks.

'You're joking, right?'

He points down the road, in the direction of the town.

'It's a holy place,' he says to Ralph, slow enough so the lad will understand. 'A shrine. People go there to say prayers and get healed. Like Lourdes.'

'Ah,' Ralph says.

'Like Medjugorje.'

'Yes, okay, yeah, I know.'

'Want to stop?'

Ralph's eyebrows go up, his mouth forms a comic-dour pout of consideration, his brow comes down again, he tilts his head from side to side. He can't assess whether Brendan is serious, and then he sees the glint in Brendan's eye. He smiles a broad gleaming smile. *Fuck,* Brendan thinks, admiring the whiteness and straightness of his teeth. Ralph's laugh is a girlish giggle that unfolds with familiarity, devoid of inhibition.

'Nah, is okay,' he says. 'I don't feel like to pray right now.'

'Me neither,' says Brendan. 'I could do with a bit of holy water though.'

'You're not a religious fella?' Ciara says, catching Ralph's eye in the rear-view mirror.

'Am I religious?'

'Yeah. That's what I'm asking.'

'Not religious, no,' Ralph says. 'Spiritual, more like, you know?'

'Spiritual?'

'Yes.'

'That's nice.'

'Yeah, is nice, I suppose. It's like… I believe, you know… but not in God or Jesus… just… I don't know… maybe I believe in the universe or something.'

'He believes in the universe! Did you hear that, Brendo?'

'I heard it,' Brendan says.

Ciara looks like she might cry.

'He's so sweet,' she says.

'Turn the radio up,' Brendan says.

When they pass the lorry cab, Ciara gives an audacious little toot and waves her hand out the window.

'Don't provoke him!' Brendan says.

'It's like Thelma and Louise,' Ciara says.

Brendan can't be bothered to point out the notable differences. Instead he turns to Ralph.

'Have you sampled the Guinness yet?'

'What? Guinness?'

'Yeah. Black stuff. Creamy head on top.'

'No I don't like.'

Brendan and Ciara hit a spontaneously synchronised groan.

'It's very heavy, very strong,' Ralph says.

'What a pussy!' Brendan says, disgusted.

'The poor boy only weighs about eight stone. What *do* you drink then?'

'I prefer the Swiss beer. The lager.'

'Sure.' Under her breath Ciara says, 'we'll soon knock that out of him. He'll be a Guinness swigging alco by the time he leaves this place.'

'What do you think of our food?' Brendan asks. 'It's shit isn't it?'

'Food is nice,' Ralph says.

'Yeah?'

'Breakfast is really cool.'

'Oh.'

'I love this eggs, sausage—how you call it—rasher?'

'Ah, now you're talking. Are you hungry now?'

'Angry? No, I'm not angry.'

'Hungry. Food. Now?'

'Sorry, sorry. For me, these two words are confused always.'

'Easy mistake to make,' Ciara says drily. 'Not like narcolepsy and necrophilia.'

'Don't embarrass me in front of the lad,' Brendan says.

'What?' says Ralph leaning forward.

'Never mind,' they say.

They continue on towards Claregalway, Ralph straining to get a look at the view through Helen's jumbled possessions. The road is narrow and the landscape is flat with only lock-ups and abandoned petrol stations and ugly bungalows and sweeping fields that are flat and forlorn. The famous stonewalls begin to appear like perforations on a page; tantalising boundaries that demarcate field upon field, their purpose negligible, but their arrangement quaint. Ciara points them out for Ralph who looks, and shows a surprising amount of interest. Ciara has noticed that the cab driver is tailing her closely now, seemingly intent on finding his way past her again; his disdain for her one-litre engine evident in the way he sways across her back bumper, his headlights sitting high and close in her rear-view mirror.

'So he is a cunt after all,' Brendan says, lighting up another fag.

'He was driving much slower earlier,' Ciara says.

'Was probably texting his girlfriend or something. Now he wants to get you back for your cheek.'

'I was only teasing. Having a bit of fun,' she says.

'On the road there is no such thing as a bit of fun. People become other creatures behind the wheel, haven't you noticed that?'

'I dunno,' she says. 'Anyway, I'm gonna fecking let him pass when I get a chance to pull in.'

'Fuck him. Let him wait. He shouldn't be intimidating you.'

Ralph remains silent. He is tired of the view and has reverted to his phone, messaging and scrolling, probably updating somebody on the progress of his trip.

'What're you gonna do when you get to Galway?' Brendan asks idly, blowing smoke with less concern for its escape out of the window. Ciara lets out a dry cough in the tobaccoed fog.

'I have friends,' Ralph says. 'Two guys I met in Bolivia.'

'Fuck me,' says Brendan. 'You were in Bolivia?'

'Yeah, it was pretty cool.'

'Are the people nice?'

'Oh for sure,' says Ralph.

Brendan's primary concern on visiting any new place is for the candour of its people, above everything else: scenery, food, drink, nightlife, cost...

'One day I would like to return,'

'Yeah? Don't you have other places on your bucket list? I bet you do.'

'Bucket list?'

'Yeah, you know... things you want to do, places you want to see, before you die.'

In days, months and years to come, Brendan, who has never been superstitious, will wonder whether, with these few words, he somehow determined Ralph's fate; whether he had not, in fact, precipitated his untimely death by the very movement of his lips, the very utterance of the word *die* at the exact moment that the kitten appeared on the road. He has heard subsequently of the *Butterfly Effect*, in which the world is determined and altered, its course changed in every instant, by every fragile pulse, by every breeze that blows, by every beat of wings; every blink, nudge, sigh, breath. He hears repeated in his head his own voice, saying *before you die*, over and over, and with this audio recording, which is like a tape spooling through his brain, he has burnished on his retina the visual sequence that starts and restarts like a stop-motion animation, and which is triggered each time by the words that preceded it. *Before you die.*

He didn't see the kitten that Ciara braked so hard to save, because he was turned in the passenger's direction, staring him straight in the eye, and the image of that eye has stayed intact, although the body in one fraction of a second was gone—untethered by any belt—and in its place was the illogical, impossible headlight of the lorry. The sound, while it must have been thunderous, otherworldly, apocalyptic, left no trace; nothing he can remember at all. He only hears the perpetual echo of the words: *Before you die.* And he turns his head to see Ciara on the road already, but standing, her mouth open. And Ralph on the ground at her feet. His intestine—so unbelievably long—is coiled around the base of the tall lamp and seems indistinguishable from the flex, which is dangling over the bonnet of the car, its three-pinned plug facing up like a baby's hand.

It is he who should be to blame, he will tell Ciara later, although she cannot, and never will, accept this. Or the cab driver... But no. And while they each wrangle with this dilemma, he asks himself: What if we had left at half-past ten as planned? What if we had never picked up the Swiss boy? What if we had told Helen to collect her own fucking things? What if she had never moved to Galway at all?

The Kowloon Bridge

Each summer we would walk to the cliffs
where you can see Toe Head and The Stags
surging from the ocean like a drowning hand.
My father would bring the binoculars to his eyes,
saying, 'At low tide they say you can see it,
the tip of a funnel.' He'd scan the sea
like a captain watching for a storm.
'I remember the night it went down.
You were that size,' he showed me with a hand.
'We were up poles all night. Half of the country switched out.
Every bloody crew in the country were up poles.'
I asked him if it went fast. 'Twenty minutes.'
He clicked his fingers and my stomach clenched
into a knot. As if it had just happened.
He handed me the binoculars and I watched
snakes of light as they played on the sea,
silent slaps of white on the death black rock.
I held my breath for a shape or a fleck of colour,
something to mark the grave. But nothing.
We'd walk back the two miles to our caravan
where my mother would have new spuds
piled on a dish for anyone to take. And each
summer it was the same—the first two weeks of July,
when the beaches and caravan parks
were suffocated with the laughter of children.
He'd want to go out to the cliffs, to walk
the two miles of fuchsia and honeybees
and tractors twisting hay into bales.
The binoculars swinging like a grandfather clock
on his chest. Hoping to catch a glimpse
of what it means to go under for the last time.

Aidan O'Donoghue

Egg Breathing

You brought me warm, brown ovals
one for each month of her life

they lay in my palms
three small worlds

first we used a pin to prick them
I reached in with a needle

pierced the yolk and broke the membrane
but it was you

who put them to your mouth
whose lips met the paper-thin resist

bone and sorrow
and you breathed

till they were light and empty
lanterns

Pippa Little

Samson and Goliath

Of course they only built two:
in Belfast you're either one
or the Other
(now both defunct,
but still giving bother).

Nathan Thanki

St Anne's Cathedral

A defiantly electric reach
into the stone-grey sky
like the class joker
raising their hand
in anticipation of laughter
—and what could be funnier
than this city's contradictions
and celebrated disasters?

Nathan Thanki

RE:fresh | David Wheldon

Aiden O'Reilly

Like many others, I ended up in London in the late 80s when I finished the Leaving Certificate. By day I worked for a plastering contractor called Rudy Blackhawk on a site close to Battersea Power Station. Rudy was black, married to a Connemara woman, and his workers were, if it needs to be said, almost all Irish. Rudy was adept at coping with their turbulent mood swings, ferry-acquired skills, and casual racism. The whole 'County Kilburn' London-Irish scene felt like a jaded theme park, yet many nights I ended up there playing along. I can't have had much time for reading, yet I seem to have read a lot: Hesse, Quine, Beckett, T.S. Eliot, Dostoyevsky, Conrad, Swift.

As was my habit at the time, my eye would alight on books that held promise of unlocking secrets of how the world works. Books described as ground-breaking or probing or uncompromising. At a bookstall at Camden market this blurb intrigued me: *When the letter came, inviting Alexander to attend an unspecified course of instruction, he somehow felt oddly compelled to attend. From that moment on, his world changed, all of his certainties and logic called into question.* The book was David Wheldon's *The Course of Instruction*, and had been published only a year before. It was one of the few contemporary books I read at that time.

Alexander is not sure what to make of the invitation. The director at the lab where he works takes a glance at it and grants him permission to take time off work. Alexander travels to the specified small industrial town and soon finds the address: a heavily elegant, tall red-brick house. He cannot immediately locate anyone in charge, and runs up against incompetence and confusion and servants hustling for tips. After several pages of this, Alexander gets round to asking blunt questions: 'Do you know anything about the course of instruction?' He considers getting the next train back to the city, but then he imagines the embarrassment of explaining what has happened to his boss. And so he stays, getting further embroiled in speculations and prevarications. The atmosphere is far from foreboding: Alexander is at times sarcastic, rude to badly-dressed staff, gets impatient at incompetence, and yet dozens of pages into the novel he is still there, still trying to establish contact with the correct authority. I well recall a growing sense of eeriness, an intensifying feeling of being suffocated. As the saying goes, if you put a frog in a pot of water and slowly turn up the heat, it will boil to death without jumping out. I wanted to shout, 'Get out. Just leave.'

When in fact Alexander does just that, I had a palpable sense of relief. I also had an intimation that this novel was devious beyond my comprehension. Alexander goes into the town, enquires about cheap hotels, starts drinking with some business reps, gets drunk in a pub lock-in. And, with no clear decision being made, ends up back at the house again.

I wondered—rather ridiculously—if perhaps the author hadn't had any intention of conveying horror, but that this was entirely my own misplaced reaction. Perhaps I was reading a novel different to the one the author had typed, although the words were identical.

On the next renovation I worked on, there was a plasterer from Vietnam. Building workers were generally English or Irish, with Polish and Russian counting as exotic. This Vietnamese man was such an anomaly he inevitably attracted a second glance. In the café—more accurately 'the kaff'—at lunch break I asked him what religion he was. 'Back in Vietnam I am Buddhist, but here—' he indicated London all around him, 'here I believe in *nothing*.' He said the word with a peculiar vehemence.

There, in London, authenticity was something remote, to be sought out in the small fields of Tây Nguyên or Mayo and exploited for a very authentic novel. Wheldon's fictions spoke to me: the elusive nature of identity that pervades all his characters and the surreal unspecified settings mapped more accurately to reality as I experienced it.

When I re-read *The Course of Instruction* two decades later I was impressed by the hallucinatory precision of the writing. Like the films of Tarkovsky, we encounter images and impressions that bear a dream-like latent significance. There is almost an over-precise awareness of the space around the characters, of muffled sounds, gestures that may or may not have significance.

The novel is full of off-kilter observations. One frail servant is depicted: 'Her voice hardly raised an echo from the glossy walls. "They can never leave the subject alone," she said, mechanically, as though rapid speech might help her preserve her balance.' An official is described: 'He took a pace towards Alexander but checked himself, as though he were a dog at the end of a running chain.'

The feeling of horror was much diminished. On a second reading I agreed with Alexander that it is impossible for him to return to his unexamined work life ('the routine mode of a routine life with ambitions which were no longer worth while'). There is nothing horrific about the House, though it may represent a path of thought that is of no practical use.

A religious interpretation of the letter Alexander receives, which had not occurred to me before, now seemed blindingly obvious. Many receive the call, each has to interpret it in their own way, it can be ignored if you wish, and so on. The House might represent the contemplative life, and the letter a religious vocation, or whatever the correlate might be in a secular world.

I was struck by a surprising parallel with George Herbert's 'The Collar'. In the poem, Herbert—convincingly to the modern ear—argues that he is a free man and not a slave to his faith: 'Forsake thy cage, / Thy rope of sands, / Which pettie thoughts have made, and made to thee / Good cable, to enforce and draw, / And be thy law'. In an alternative reading of the novel, Alexander's periodic appeals to common sense ('Do you think I'm restrained in this house like a dog?') are not isolated moments of clarity, but instead are empty bluster.

When I first read it I wasn't aware of how the novel is laced through with existentialist concerns: engagement, authenticity, the ongoing creation of one's self. Such concepts form a shared cultural background of much Central European fiction from the 1930s onward, and it would be wrong to suggest these writers were all reading their Sartre and Heidegger. If there is an overt philosophical alignment in Wheldon's novel, it is rather to Wittgenstein. There is a preoccupation with interpretations of what has been written or said. The ability of language to communicate is constantly in doubt, characters launch into convoluted deliberations only to dismiss them as empty reasoning. The servants, he learns from an ally in the house, keep a phrase book for better communication with visitors. 'Because they do speak the same language it's easy for us to fall into the trap of believing that they think in much the same way as ourselves.'

The Course of Instruction was Wheldon's second novel, and some months after reading it I sought out his debut work, *The Viaduct*. A released prisoner, referred to as *A* except for two scenes where he is called Alexander, has nowhere to go and follows the disued railway track above the city. He is initially pursued: the authorities have drummed up some secondary charge to put him back in jail. *A* meets up with other travellers on the railway, and learns the customs and superstitions of this way of life. He joins up with a tall man who first took to the railway because his family was embarrassed about his epileptic fits. The tall man has a pathologically shy companion, who relates how there was a time when he was unable to speak to people for shyness, and used to observe them and imagine conversations. He too had his reasons for leaving his previous settled life. 'The area was pointless, and its religion, and the way in which people lived. There was decency, but it was a decency born of cant.'

It's a sort of *Wizard of Oz* for the existentially inclined, no disrespect to either book. It's written in a stark confident prose that is at odds with the subtlety of the thoughts being conveyed. There is an immediacy to the characters, there is plot and tension, and yet they are not realistic in any conventional sense. To be precise, they are not familiar characters such as we meet every day. Reading the novel is like a close encounter with thinking creatures who are almost, but not quite, the same as ourselves, and in the process we come to realise how strange we are.

The story is immensely quotable and resists any single interpretation. The paucity of similar fiction, on such a serious level, leaves the reader grasping for comparable works: Beckett's two tramps on their barren wasteland keep coming back to mind, Kafka's castle, several fictions from Borges, some of Ishiguro's novels.

There's an amusing story about the similarity to Kafka. Wheldon swears he had never read a word of Kafka before writing the novel. He wrote it using a clunky ancient typewriter, which was a bit of a strain on his fingertips. To save effort, he typed *A* for Alexander, thinking that if it ever got published the full name could be inserted then. But as he wrote the text it developed a loose poetry of its own. The character began to inhabit his one-letter name. When the novel was finished Wheldon realised that substituting 'Alexander' would ruin the rhythm. Some early reviewers latched on to the $K <> A$ parallel, and coupled with a perceived similarity in style, criticised the novel for being too obviously derivative.

There are overlaps with Wheldon's concerns in *The Course of Instruction*: the extent to which our thoughts and mannerisms are borrowed from others, the instability of our self-image, a heightened awareness of how people can have fundamentally differing natures. *The Viaduct* is more fable-like and proceeds with greater speed. Both novels involve the protagonist moving to a place where established ways of thinking prove fragile. Both have an unspecified setting; architecture and some customs are recognisably English, but there is no mention of place names.

It would be hard to argue that Wheldon's novels were under-appreciated when they first appeared. *The Viaduct* won the Triple First Award and attracted praise from Graham Greene and William Trevor. Both received glowing reviews in major newspapers and were also published in the USA. And yet an internet search throws up almost no references to Wheldon's fiction. Google 'David Wheldon' and you will come across discussions of The Wheldon Protocol for the treatment of multiple sclerosis. It's the same person, though it takes some online detective work to verify this. Wheldon is a medical doctor who specialises in infections of the central nervous system, and has recently retired. He continues to write, and has published two more novels, *A Vocation* and *At the Quay*, and several books of poetry, as well as numerous uncollected short stories.

Interest in Wheldon's work has revived recently. *Confingo* magazine is publishing several of his stories sequentially, and his fictions will also appear in Nightjar Press and Woven Tale Press.

That First Year

The world spun on—
same rotation from West to East,
same speed, same seasons
in the same order.

Tides did their usual thing,
waves made their lapping sounds,
seagulls screeched their indignation.

Over in No. 80
small changes were noted:

the kitchen table
listing to one side,

no back and forth
of a conversation
sixty years
in the making.

Elsewhere:

the faint sound of
uilleann pipes,
slide guitars,
pianos playing
traditional laments,

and Louis Armstrong
having to remind us
it's a wonderful world.

Anne Tannam

Tech House

Lisa McInerney

So it's like this, says Neil. We strike.

This is put to his co-workers in the confusion of their thirty-minute lunch break, as people gulp, suck, chew, pick, choke, swallow. Thirty minutes to get through the detectors and security lines, eat, drink, make phone calls to babysitters, use the bathroom, stretch, get back through the detectors again. There is little time to make sense of this call to arms, though the others seem to have been expecting it; Leona looks around her and notes their nodding, their acknowledging murmurs.

The plans are made in voices very low. Management won't budge, Neil says, but we cannot threaten to strike, even the mention of protest would be received as an inclination towards revolt, what's become of this bloody country at all? There are too many of us, Neil goes on, to sack in one go. The whole town outside couldn't fill the ranks as fast as they'd be emptied. There is strength in numbers.

The workers look at watches. They wolf down what's left, run for the bathroom stalls, put their mobile phones back in their lockers, pop their pills. They queue to get back into the warehouse. They pick up their scanners. They take deep breaths.

Leona works in a building the size of an aircraft hangar. It is filled with all manner of discounted products to be purchased online: coffee capsules, eye shadow palettes, car mats, water filter systems. It is a place of patterns, in which things are counted incessantly. The counting is done by computer; people cannot be trusted with the task or with the items; people have short attention spans and sticky fingers. The orders are assigned to the workers via their scanners. When Leona started working here she was told to leave everything but the clothes on her back in her locker and she was given a scanner. She had been surprised by its weight. She is still surprised by its weight.

And sure what good is it? her mother asked.

It keeps track of everything, Leona said. It tells you what things to get, and it tells you where to find the things. It even tells you how many minutes exactly it should take to find them.

The scanner counts the units, the minutes taken, the metres run. When Leona falls behind, supervisors arrive, mantis-like and nervous, and tell her that she has to work harder. The orders have to be filled. The customers must not wait. The machine spins and spins.

Before every shift Leona swallows two Ibuprofen tablets. This is for the pain. The bins in which the items are stored are stacked ten-high. Stretching for the highest bins is grand, it's the stooping for the bins on the floor that's the problem. Up down, up down. No Olympian is asked to move like this. Halfway through her very first day Leona was open-mouthed with the shock of it. Jesus, it really takes it out of you, she muttered, and a supervisor said, You get used to it, but she never got used to it, and as the days went on she noted that the supervisor said this to all the new people.

You don't get used to it, Neil corrected, soon enough. The only thing is to take painkillers.

Neil is forty-six, stocky and gruff, and has come to the notion of striking as though irritated into action by his colleagues' helplessness. He seems not at all paternal, though he has two grandchildren. Leona wonders if Neil's daughter buys from places like this. Toys and books, polo shirts for playschool, brightly coloured storage boxes, Christmas baubles. She wonders if Neil has ever felt his tendons strain as he pulled some geegaw in plastic wrap, purchased by kin, out of a floor-level bin? Does he go home at night and weep, No more, please, shop local, I'd much rather die in penury than pain? Is he a different man outside of this place? Does he drink stout and laugh at jokes?

Leona does not relay the goings-on of her workplace at home. There is rarely anything to discuss, the goings-on are so repetitive. Just orders given through the scanner and filled through the scanner. Just jogging, stretching, squatting and silence. They are not supposed to converse in case it slows them down but this is a self-governing sort of rule: they all move too fast to converse, and slowing down means black marks on their files.

Tell them they can fuck off, says Leona's mother. All of them. Tell them they do not dictate to you. Tell them I'm on to them. Tell them I know well what goes on. Tell them.

Leona lives with her mother and her mother isn't well and isn't right. This job, Leona hopes, will provide the means of getting out. She thinks, Maybe three months and they'll promote me to mantis-slash-supervisor. I will earn one-seventy an hour more, which adds up. She will have enough for a deposit and a month's rent in some little apartment. Three months would be plenty—staff turnover is high. Many people leave and don't come back; Leona images them as Inuit heading into the blind white wilderness to die privately so their collapse does not prove dispiriting for the team. Many more people are fired. Here they give you black marks for any number of infractions. Bringing your phone onto the warehouse floor. Being more than a minute late getting through the detectors. Taking a day off because of bereavement or illness or terrorist siege. Leona imagines these black marks as splashes of tar; they stick and glisten and you need only a small amount before you are lost altogether. But at least the rules are clear. You can't pretend you didn't know.

Leona's son, Mason, is twenty months old. She leaves him with their neighbour Dympna when she goes to work. This upsets her mother and Leona must make up sweet excuses for the snub. I don't want you to think of him as work, is the main one, but the excuses generally do not work, and her mother becomes belligerent, and cannot see that this belligerence is the reason she is not allowed the run of her grandson's life. She's not well and she's not right. There are clinical terms that change with medical advances and her mother's chosen doctor. There are pills that take the edge off it, but there are no pills she'll take for long enough. Since Leona was small a nursery rhyme has looped inside her in relation to her mother's disposition: *When she was good, she was very, very good, but when she was bad…* she would scream, rant and rave; she would put every coin she had into the poker machine in Brady's; she would accuse all those she saw of monstrous crimes; she would find God and then the devil and once she'd found the devil there wasn't a cranny he wouldn't have wedged himself into or a ledge she wouldn't spot him on.

That baby's grandfather was a filthy man, Leona's mother said, time and time again when Leona was pregnant. He used watch the girls get changed. That's why he worked in the community centre, so he could watch the girls get changed. Both the priests knew about it and neither did a thing. Filthy, dirty article, he was. That baby's grandfather.

Though the workers are twisted by the physical demands of their employ—some bear scars from the edges of towers, ladders, beams and bins—Leona tries hard to see sense in the job's patterns. The codes to be scanned. The specific projections for steps required to get from here to there. The swiftness of it and the silence of it. It is like being in the belly of a mechanical titan, like being a drop of lurid colour about to sink into a gunmetal sea. She thinks it could be simple surrender, at the heart of it. Or geometric order. Or conquering numbers, an education in straight, perfect lines. There might even be a sort of dance to it, though they are not permitted to listen to music on the warehouse floor.

When her shift finishes, Leona collects Mason and walks the eleven steps from Dympna's front door to front gate and then the eleven steps from her own front gate to her own front door. I'll see you tomorrow so, pet, says Dympna, still on her doorstep, looking out at the green and the terriers and the teenagers. Dympna says 'pet' but only as a subconscious suffix; she doesn't make a pet of anyone. She's a woman who missed a step somewhere along the line, and life has never allowed her to slow down enough to correct it.

Leona does not tell her mother about the planned strike. There is no space at home for supplementary sources of anxiety; her mother needs only the one nudge. Instead tonight they listen to the man on the radio, who is discussing poetry with two women who speak in the melodic tones so suited to the arts, like the Confessional but with the odd drop of sauce.

Isn't that beautiful? Leona says of the featured poem.

I don't know what it was about, her mother says.

The point is that it sounds beautiful, Leona says.

Before Mason, Leona almost always went out on Saturday nights. She used to knock about with a couple of girls she thought of then as friends; she knows now they only ever met up for the specific purpose of going out on Saturday nights. Gillian Mooney was one and Alannah O'Dea was the other. Each suspected they didn't have that much in common, except tech-house and flat shoes.

Gillian and Alannah were both fond of stimulants. Fuel, they laughed. Keeps you on your feet all night. Leona never felt that way about drugs. Drugs do not keep you on your feet all night: drugs keep you chewing the ears off strangers in the toilets and bumming cigarettes from irritated bouncers. She never liked the loss of control that goes with doing drugs. The wildness of it is what appeals to others, she knows. The loss of inhibition allows them to focus on the rhythms of dance music. We are not tribes anymore so it is hard to think tribally. It is hard to follow tribal rhythms. It is hard to remember how to react to drums.

All Leona wanted from Saturday nights was to react to drums. She always found it easy to follow the pattern. What you do is this: take a spot on the floor, take metrical baby steps, keep your elbows in. Punch the air directly above you. Keep in time with the swelling, spilling mass of your temporary compatriots. Heave as one, like a murmuration. Sweat.

There are guards always in that place, her mother said. It's only rotten with drug dealers and criminals and rapists and pickpockets. Don't tell me nothing goes on, don't I know what goes on?

No, Mam. I swear. There's never trouble there.

Leona could still go out on Saturday nights. Dympna has suggested that she do so, the odd time. But in that scenario Leona's mother would have some influence over her grandson's care; between herself and Dympna they'd have to divvy up the Saturday nights. Leona's mother does not think of herself as being untrustworthy, and in her clearest, happiest state there is no better woman, no matter the task. But so quickly she flips.

Dympna knows all about Leona's mother. Sure amn't I well able for her, she has said to Leona, though Leona suspects that Dympna's experience of being well able has always been down to luck. There is a wry cosmic joke in the sweetly ignorant coming in at just the right sparse times to make sense of one or two of Leona's mother's inner evils. You are in your hole well able for her, Leona has wanted to reply, you're just a jammy ould bitch. But then Leona is determined not to have it in her to be cruel.

So instead, when Leona gets Mason fed and bathed and into bed and read to, she closes the door and runs an old coat along the bottom of it, and she puts her headphones on and closes the curtains, and she presses play and closes her eyes, and she starts to nod, and she starts to dance.

She has lost Gillian and Alannah. They are not interested in her as a working mother and they would think bedroom dancing weird. Even in the age of Upworthy and Buzzfeed in which people click endlessly on displays curated to inspire and stir, they would think bedroom dancing weird; even in the age of Lena Dunham and Beyoncé and you-do-you, they would think bedroom dancing weird, particularly if they knew that Leona did it every weekend, in her socks on the carpet, as a scheduled reconnection to positive rhythms.

But tonight Leona does not find it easy to catch the rhythm. She is thinking of the planned strike, of Neil's dragging them into battle because he feels it is right that they battle. She closes her eyes and listens hard. She cannot even put her back into it; her back is killing her. She knows that Neil is right and that his cause is noble but that doesn't make it less frightening, for how then will she get away? If the job goes where does that leave her? She begins to count beats. Four-four, four-four. She focuses on configurations of notes and logical musical progression. She visualises the shapes in her mindfulness colouring-book. And lastly heartbeats, the mathematical rhythms of her body.

The coat on the floor inside the door rucks. Leona doesn't see it, turned the other way, eyes closed on this rotation, but she hears the thump of fist-flats on the white gloss wood, and now she must take her headphones off and take up Mason and tell her mother, who is red with indignation, that she'll talk to her as soon as she settles the child.

You shouldn't bang on the door, Mam.

You shouldn't be bouncing around like a fucking lunatic. What are you listening to that makes you lep around like that? Computer music, isn't that it? Music to listen to when you're off your head on drugs, isn't that it? What are you listening to? What are you listening to? What are you listening to?

In the morning Neil gathers them in the car park in front of the warehouse doors. We don't stay home, he says, we stay here. That way they have to engage us. That way there's a mass of us and a mass attracts attention. Teddy here's going to take photographs for the social media. We'll get on to the papers. It's a bigger thing this way. Don't you go in there, he warns newcomers.

The workers become cheerfully riled as Neil speaks. The business model here must be adjusted to reflect that it needs real people to implement it, and real people are messy and contradictory things, have corporeal needs and limitations, real people are not robots. There is a cheer. We are not asking for the earth, only for our rights. Another, more assured cheer. They cannot sack all of us, it is in their interests to get us back inside, but we do not go back inside until our demands are met. And true to logical progression this gets the biggest cheer of all. Leona's co-workers give each other thumbs up. They draw from each other gall and guts. A chant comes together. Some of the workers are taking photographs, tweeting, texting, and phoning. Management is called and a representative attempts to mollify the workers and get them indoors. Think of your children, this manager says. Think of Christmas coming.

Think of our futures, Neil says, is that it? Or this shift only, today's targets?

Christmas has me kilt, a woman cries.

And there's a surge. Leona takes metrical steps backwards. She folds her shoulders to make herself smaller.

C'mere to me, a stór, he wasn't right for you anyway, her mother said. You're from stock that lad's stock wasn't even good enough to serve soup to. You've a royal heart in you, you're tuned to the music of the spheres, you have a pure soul, and you mustn't let him drag on you.

This gets out of hand, as is told in the very definition of revolution: nothing is won without risk, and change is the root of all fortune. Briefly, Leona feels sick at the idea. She tries to be aware of her heartbeats, the mathematical rhythms of her body (this is a place of patterns, in which things are counted incessantly).

She breaks and cries out and steps towards the main doors and Neil closes one fist around her arm. Don't listen to them, he says, and his voice is transformed: it is deeper, like it has bubbled up from within him. Leave her go, says a manager, and lays his hands too and there is brief and violent disarray.

We're doing this for the likes of her, Neil says. You lot exploit the young wans, you'd grind them all into the ground and not think twice about it.

Mind! shouts the manager.

We mind each other! Neil shouts back.

For a second it is as if Leona might fall.

She is kept on her feet by the swelling, spilling mass of her co-workers.

They heave as one, like a murmuration.

There is a pulse to this. A sense of organic machinery.

The chanting is stronger. People have gotten into the rhythm of it.

Are you all right, Leona? Neil asks. Stay here with us. We'll be fine if we stick together.

I'm all right, Leona says. I think I'm getting the hang of it now.

Deluge

Water rushes down the hill behind the house.
It pools on the ground when there's nowhere left to go,
pushes its way under the hall door.
Dark stains bloom on the kitchen walls.
Cracks emerge. Plaster bloats. The chimney breast weeps.

A horse appears from nowhere in the neighbouring field.
At night his white coat gleams on the dark hillside.
By day he turns his rump to us and huddles against the ditch.
His broad back drips. His coat turns dull grey.
I bring him gifts—apples, carrots—I cannot stay away.

The rain falls and falls. The horse's ribs appear.
He tramples the food I bring into the sodden soil.
I picture him in my kitchen, his hooves thick with mud,
his flanks and shoulders shuddering with terror and relief.
I watch the rain steal his last trace of white.

He's barely visible now, even in daylight.
I mourn his muscled neck, his powerful limbs and glossy coat.
I watch him fade away. He is too weak to raise his head.
At night my ghost horse haunts me, a shade in a dark field.
You failed me, his phantom whispers. I needed more than gifts.

Emer Fallon

Berry Fever

For Caroline

The blackberries ripen early this year. I leave the house
laden with boxes and bowls and find women combing
hedgerows and fields, berry lust deep in their eyes.

You ring to tell me they've harvested the eggs.

I visit shadowed places I've never been before
and stumble across dark droppings outside some animal's den.
The air smells musky and unknowable. I run.

Meanwhile you sniff hormones, inject yourself.
At night a badger rampages through my dreams.
By day I snuffle my way through ferns and rotting grass.

Some berries are already on the wrong side of ripe.
Others have been annexed by a thin mucous veil.
These ones make my stomach turn. But still I cannot stop.

You will hear tomorrow if the eggs took.

Next morning I get up. In the mirror I am a foreign creature,
dark-eyed and wild with berry fever.
A deep white stripe cuts through the centre of my crown.

My lips are stained dark purple. My nails are ragged claws.
I smell the berries souring, in the kitchen, on the floor.
There are berries everywhere. There will never be enough.

Emer Fallon

Brushing Yonder

If you go north, it will get worse.
Valleys won't aid you.
The sun always goes down.
If you go west, you'll stumble.
All that reticence is fooling your shoes.
The moon hides in trenches.
If you go south, you'll drown, eventually.
You'll swell, you'll swivel, then flail
and capsize. It's always stormy.
If you go east, you'll survive.
But scarcely. There's no food.
The greens are dying, substances
rise and cover up the sky.

What if you stay here?
The hedge is full, the air blooms.
We're shot with care and perfume
of bare living, as roses rustle
parrots mass in yonder.
I could take your arm, nothing
banishes sorrow but that's no matter.
How root lives with skin
is the argument. There's always more
where apricots fall and lemons are flush
when you can almost believe, though
that's not enough.

It's what is more certain like a sun
like a phase, like a trice, a sudden brush
of direction. To dream of escape is
to form up the real and open your eyes
as if it was—again—morning.

Jill Jones

Stains

Something leaks into the earth
outside your window.
You hear it at night or early morning.
You see how it stains the walls
and the concrete.

It's more than a dream.
You wake and feel it tickling
and grinding your skin and hair.
The problem is not about habit, exactly.
The night could free you
if it wasn't so cool, or so hot.

You can't escape your structure
maybe you can distract the scaffold
and feed your tastes, your failed
breath and veins, nerves
that light up agony.

Falling is nothing like it, there's no
new fashion that can copy hurt.
Sometimes it's early.
The train rattles like your bones.
The train goes somewhere else.

There's nothing you can take
up a mountain, a mountain is a myth
and so is a path.
You sit and stand, nothing
makes a difference.

The times have become stiff
like drinks or drought, little deserts.
Lie down in the gutter.
Feel how it all comes back at you.

Jill Jones

Lying on a Beach

Colm O'Shea

Later she'll tell me I write like I speak. I sent her a short story. She hasn't finished it yet and left it behind in a friend's house. But she'll tell me I write like I speak.

We agreed we'd meet in the cathedral yard, by the iron gate close to the Tube station. I'm early. Jane's late. She texted to say she might be; she's coming from a hairdressing appointment. It's Sunday morning but she's nearby and won't be too late. I'm early. Misjudging the distances. Misjudging the trains. It doesn't really matter, no more than ten minutes. Yesterday was better, yesterday was warm, clear skies and a cool breeze blowing down the river. Yesterday I was nearby too, across the river being photographed by my Scottish photographer friend. Yesterday I was photographed along the riverbank because my Scottish photographer friend is trying to practise portraits. Yesterday I was trying to look thoughtful and deep, not scowling as usual. This morning I'm trying to stay dry. It's been raining. It still is. It drizzles. At the iron gate I look at the map mounted in a frame, still surprised how close some of the city really is. The Tube distorts, even after all this time. I move between the map mounted in the frame and the overhang of a nearby tree when the drizzle starts again. I'm looking for her. I'm waiting for her. I don't know which way her appointment is so I don't know where she'll come from. She might follow me from the Tube or she might cross the road where the cyclist is checking a tyre.

The cathedral looms over everything. The scale still gets me. I've been here before. I've been inside before. I don't remember paying the last time I went in but somebody mentioned that they now charge admittance. I don't know. I don't think we're going in today. I wait for her. If it was dry I could sit on the bench. If it was dry I could sit on the bench and browse on my phone and at least I wouldn't be checking out everyone who passes. Everyone who passes putting on rain gear. Most are tourists, who else wanders around this part of the city at this time on a Sunday? They look at me as they pass. I look at them, waiting for her. They might wonder why the scruffy looking man in the tweed blazer is standing near the gate staring at them or staring at the gate or staring at the map mounted in the frame or sheltering under a tree. It's more of a big bush. No, it's probably a tree. It does the job though. I should have borrowed a raincoat; I should have brought an umbrella. If the rain gets worse at least we could both shelter under an umbrella. It doesn't get worse and it doesn't get better. A low, slight drizzle, in for the day. Soft day. So I wait. Of course it feels like she's later than she is because I'm waiting and because I'm early and because it's damp, but she's not late. No more than a few minutes really.

She appears by the end of the cathedral. She emerges and she smiles. I step out from under the tree. She's wearing that beret again. That scarlet beret. She shouldn't be walking around the back of a cathedral in the drizzle in that beret. She should be chained to a gate in the sunshine with a cigarette sticking to her lips in that beret. She smiles. I don't care about the drizzle. Later. Much later. In another city another woman with another pretty face will pass me by wearing another scarlet beret and I'll nearly walk into a lamppost. She smiles. Her small, sharp features. Her high cheekbones. Her little dusting of freckles across her nose. Her quick, inquisitive mouth and her hungry blue eyes. Walking towards me, slender calves and ankles and a pair of black high heels on her small feet, dancer's feet, walking towards me. She's much smaller than me so when we reach each other in the cathedral yard beside the cross I put my arms around her and envelop her. Well that is what I want.

We make quick chit-chat. I'm well. She's well. She's sorry she's a little late but the hairdresser had another appointment. I tell her I don't mind. She's not late at all. We walk. We agreed to meet. We agreed to have lunch. But we didn't know where. So we walk. We walk by the side of the cathedral and out beside the main entrance, the main steps. The colossal entrance to the cathedral, quiet on this damp Sunday. I presume they run services. I presume at some stage worshippers traipse in and worshippers traipse out but not to be seen right now. We don't think about it. I'm smiling. She's smiling. She's wearing a navy blue coat with a red leopard print scarf, a much better choice than my scruffy tweed blazer but she's on home soil and I had to pack. Plus it was much warmer yesterday. She asks about my day with the Scottish photographer, she asks how we got on. Apart from the tourists the place is almost deserted. Buses pass. Taxis pass. A few vans, but there aren't that many people around. I should be holding her hand. I should have my arm around her. I should at least link her arm as we walk. That walk, that divided walk with her. That walk I walk any time I walk with her. That comfortable walk with someone I've known now for years. That comfortable walk with someone I feel completely at ease with. But that walk. That walk of any man walking with a beautiful woman. That walk where you feel you have a part to play escorting this beautiful woman across the street. That walk where you feel you're being scrutinised in the second glances to see who this beautiful woman is walking with and wondering how she ended up walking with him. I tell her she's beautiful. I've told her she's beautiful and she tries to shrug it off. No, not shrug it off. She'll immediately point to the fact that she has a cold or didn't have time to do her makeup properly or defer to whatever image of beauty she carries along in her head trying to put me off. Whatever image she carries that isn't her. But I tell her she's beautiful because she is.

She laughs. She laughs at my over-sincere efforts to find the words. The words I need to tell her how beautiful she is. She'll giggle as I tie myself in knots again trying to find the words. There are words. There are words here now but when I speak the words disappear. When I need them the words slink away, gone. When I need them the words are gone so I stutter, so I stammer, so I hum and I haw and tie myself up and find the only words I find are the empty clichéd words that have been overused and eroded by time into grey indistinct blobs where they should be sharp and new.

We want somewhere to sit down. Somewhere to eat. Somewhere to get out of the drizzle.

The first place we look at is dead. Wrong time. Wrong day. This time tomorrow the place will be buzzing with financial types. The buyers. The sellers. The spenders. Above all the spenders. Today it's a ghost town. A clean, bright, new ghost town. The cathedral looks out of place among the glass and the steel. But its roots are deep. The glass and the steel will be long gone and the cathedral will still be looking over their descendants. The second place doesn't look much better. But it's still drizzling and we agree we're not likely to find any better. A little vestibule separates us from the restaurant itself with a heavy maroon curtain for no particular reason I can think of. When I pull it back enough for her to pass through the waiter springs to life. I think he's chatting up the barmaid and probably doesn't really want anyone else here. He puts on a smile but just wants to get back to what he was doing. We're seated against the far wall. A booth. A booth that'll be filled by half a dozen this time tomorrow. Today it's just us. He doesn't offer to take our coats. I take them back and hang them on the coatrack beside the heavy maroon curtain. We sit opposite each other. We smile. We talk. We relax.

First, but first. Before either of us get a chance to say anything. Before anything else, I apologise. I apologised before but this is the first time I've seen her since. I try to get my apology out of the way before my voice cracks too much. I try to say sorry for being such a complete fucking eejit before I can feel one little tear creeping over my cheekbone and disappearing into my beard. I try to say sorry before she can stop me and before I can stop myself. She says it's okay. She's said it's okay before this. She says it's fine. She already said it was fine. I know it's okay. I know it's fine. I have to say it anyway. I need to say it anyway. Even at the risk of bringing it all back up and the risk that she might stand up and collect her coat from the rack beside the heavy maroon curtain and disappear out the door. I have to say sorry again. I say sorry. She says it's fine. I tell her how bad I feel over what I did. She says she knows. She says it's fine. Again she almost laughs watching me tie myself in knots over it and I almost laugh too. But it's out of the way. I wanted it out of the way. I needed it out of the way. So.

So now we can talk. She's sitting opposite me talking and the flash of her bright red lips and her pale skin and her dark hair. They've left us; well the waiter has, so we can talk. We catch up. I want to know how she's been doing. I want to know how work has been for her. I want to know if she's been okay. The thing. The funny thing here. The funny thing here is I can remember the coat she's wearing. I can remember the beret. I can remember the dark stockings and black high heels. But I can't remember the dress she's wearing. I think it's blue? In my head now it's blue with a small pattern in, in yellow I think. Maybe a dark blue dress with small yellow flowers? I think. It's a very pretty vintage dress, I know that. It matches the rest of her outfit perfectly; I know that, it would do. But I can't remember what it looks like. I may just be thinking about a dress she wore on another occasion. I don't know. I think she's wearing a little piece of jewellery I bought her, a small stone on a chain. Yes, maybe, maybe. Maybe it's when she explains that she wants to get a better chain for the necklace, maybe get a better silver chain for the necklace, for the stone. I think so. I'm not sure. I'm distracted. Maybe this time, maybe some other time.

We talk. We enjoy talking. She'll ask me if she talks too much. I wonder if someone said something to her. I tell her she doesn't. I'm not saying it for the sake of saying it. I'm not saying it because that's what I'm expected to say. I say it because it's true. I want to hear. So we talk. So she talks. She does seem a little self-conscious about the idea so maybe someone did say something but I don't ask any more about it. I don't want to bring it back up. I want to hear her talk.

This is the part where I should be able to transcribe what it is we talk about. Repeat word for word what it is she tells me. But like the dress I can't. I know we both talk about work. I know we're both starting new jobs in the next couple of weeks so we both share that, excitement and worry. There's eagerness. There's confidence. There's uncertainty. It will all play out. So we talk about work. But we move on. Work is done. Work is out of the way.

The waiter comes back. I glance at the menu. I order the warm duck salad. I always seem to order duck when it is on a menu. She orders the same. Just water. Sparkling water I think. We both have things to do later. She has some work to do later, preparing for the week ahead. Just water this time then.

I ask her about her trip to France. I remind her about her little dream of retiring, no, not retiring, living, yes living. Living in a small farmhouse in France. *Gîte*, that's the word, *gîte*. That's the word I can't think of, *gîte*. There's always one. I do that. Words, the important words, the words I'm looking for just wander off. For the length of this particular conversation those important words don't exist. So I ask her about her plan to live in a little farmhouse in France. Her friend already has the farmhouse. Her friend has the land. Her friend will let her build a small cottage on the land. It sounds great. It sounds ideal. It sounds like everything she could want except it's too quiet. Too quiet for her. So the *gîte* might become an apartment in a French city, maybe a town. Hard to tell. Hard to pin her down. Hard for her to pin herself down. I don't have any such plans. I've no great scheme to disappear somewhere. I'm looking more and more internally. I worry about that sometimes. I look at her. I sit across the table from her and listen to her stories, listen to her plans. I listen to her describe to me again and again how she's going to squeeze the most out of life, keep moving until there's nowhere she hasn't tasted the air. She brightens up with the mention of any new experience and adventure. I listen. I smile. I laugh. I encourage her along the way. But I wonder if I'll always be the person waving someone like her off from the pier? I know my natural urge is to crawl further and further inside.

I laugh at her stories. Actually we both laugh. I can't remember but I know we both enjoy ourselves. Maybe I need a Dictaphone? We enjoy the warm duck salad and the almost empty restaurant in the shadow of the cathedral on a

Sunday, a Sunday lunchtime by this stage. She tells me about her holiday to Iceland. She tells me she's planned an adventure holiday to Iceland later in the year. She's already itching to go.

I think I tell her a funny story now. I think I tell her a funny anecdote anyway because she laughs. She laughs as she does and she does that thing where she covers her mouth. Her pretty mouth with her small white teeth and bright red lips. She laughs with her eyes. Covering her lips, covering her mouth she laughs from her eyes. I want to tell her more funny stories, I want to make her laugh again, again and again. I know what I want. She knows what I want. I know I want to crawl down under the table in the almost empty restaurant in the shadow of the cathedral and run my hands up under the skirt of the dress she's wearing. I want to run my hands up along her legs, her stockinged legs because they're stockings. On her they're stockings. I want to run my hands up her stockinged legs and feel the seams, feel the suspenders, feel the softness of her thighs as my hands reach further and further. I know and I know she knows that I want to run my hands further up her soft thighs and follow with my tongue and feel the softness and the warmth and the wetness. She uncrosses and crosses her legs under the table and one foot brushes against my shin. She smiles at me as her foot brushes my shin. She smiles because she knows. She looks me in the eye because she knows. A slow sly smile crosses her face; her foot brushes my shin again. But the restaurant is either too full or too empty to fully play it out. She spears a piece of duck with her fork, eats it and sticks out her tongue at me playfully. She knows and I know that she knows and she knows what I want and we sit at the table in the almost empty restaurant in the shadow of the cathedral and we tell each other stories and we smile and we laugh.

She's still worried that she talks too much. Again I wonder who said something to her? She worries that it makes her look silly. I don't know who these people are. She asked me once before if I thought she was fragile. Again, again it must have been something someone said to her. Someone that doesn't know her. Has to be someone that doesn't know her. I disagree. I strongly disagree. I wonder if the opinion of these anonymous people is worth more than my reassurance. Probably. Probably is. But I'd probably feel the same if I was in the same position. Is a compliment from a friend worth anything compared to a stranger's criticism? She does catch herself occasionally, worried that she does say too much, worried that I might think she's silly. I'll tell her it's not true. I'll reassure her that I always love talking to her and hearing her talk.

But maybe my compliments are empty. Maybe they're too soft? Maybe they're overwrought? Maybe it's because I cringe from any sort of compliment myself that I can't give one and make it sound sincere? Maybe that's why she doubts me? No. That's not it. She doesn't doubt me. When it comes to compliments she just doubts herself.

She tells me about a date she's been on. He sounds like an idiot. He sounds like a prick. I don't know how she met him, were they set up by someone? I don't ask. She tells me they talked about the theatre, as she does, as she loves to do, as she will use to gauge if she and he or she and whoever have anything in common and he tells her that he goes to the theatre often because he can easily afford to. I laugh. She laughs. Prick.

We move on. We talk about other things. Moving on. I ask her how she's been. I ask her because she told me before that she was ill. She's nervous. She doesn't really want to talk to me about it but she'll say something. She could say everything's fine, it's all cleared up and there's nothing to talk about and we'll move on. But when I ask her how she is I can see her thinking, considering how much she'll tell me. Would I have made a good confessor? She tells me a little. She tells me enough. She tells me she's fine. She tells me she had a biopsy and she's fine. She doesn't go into details but she tells me she's fine. She tells me just enough for me to look it up online later. I don't know whether I should or shouldn't do that. Probably not. But I can't not do it. She describes the procedure. Vague, not much detail. Getting out of the conversation as quickly as she can but she's in it now and has to tell me something. She tells me they burned her. She tells me it's the treatment. She tells me she's fine. She tells me everything's okay. They burn her. THEY. BURN. HER. I can't get those words out of my head. I can't get the idea out of my head. When I go home later. When I look it up online, which I probably shouldn't do. When I figure out the correct term for the treatment she had because she doesn't tell me the name and because she's too busy telling me she's okay. When I finally look up the right word and the right thing and I see the procedure described and I see the success rates described and the commonplace nature of it all now and I'm meant to be reassured. But they burn her. THEY. BURN. HER. I know. I know. I know she's okay. I know there's nothing wrong with her in any way at all. Still. Still.

We move on.

She asks about my writing. I try to make it sound better than it is. I try to make sitting alone late at night in the quiet with the lamp over my head more exciting than it is. But she knows. She knows.

We move on.

Time is getting on.

General things. Friendly things. Genial things. Do we chat about a movie? Do we chat about a song? I don't know. It isn't important but it leads us on. I ask her about her singing. I ask about the course she just finished. She's pleased with it all but doesn't have any plans to record anything again. Not yet anyway. Not for a while. It depends. Depends on time. Depends on work. Depends on where she goes. What way the wind will blow and where it might take her. I asked her before about taking up permanent contracts. I don't know if she just hasn't managed to be offered one yet or if she's afraid of being chained to one spot. That pilgrim soul peeks out behind those blue eyes of hers every now and then, especially when the idea of standing still comes up. She might. She will. She will when she wants. She will if she wants. She tells me she wants to record 'Blue Moon' next. She sings a few bars. Even here. Even low in the restaurant. Even here it's gorgeous. Finding the right space in every note. Finding the right space. It's like hearing her speak. Crisp. Clear. Pin-point accuracy. When she speaks, every now and then her voice slips, a little, but she corrects herself almost before I or anyone else has a chance to notice. She has created herself. She decided early on just who she wants to be. And decided no one will stop her.

Time is getting on.

We order dessert. We order a dessert. An Eton mess. Not sure we want it. Not sure I want it. I know I want to drag the time out, that's the thing. If we were drinking I'd quickly order another bottle. If we were drinking I'd use a *sure another little one won't hurt you*, something like that. But she has things to do. I have things to do. So I have to settle for the dessert. Did I mention she's wearing a cardigan? Did I say she's wearing a cardigan? Pink. Pink I think? A short, tight cardigan over the dress I can't really remember. Maybe that's why not? A short tight cardigan over her vintage dress that makes her look like a schoolteacher. That makes her look like a schoolteacher in a time none of us ever went to school in a school that never existed. But there's a look of a schoolteacher all the same.

Time is getting on.

Time to go.

I catch the waiter's eye, still chatting to the woman behind the bar at the far side of the restaurant. I catch his eye and I pay the bill.

Time to go.

He brings back my card but doesn't offer to bring back our coats. I do that myself. I help her into her navy blue coat over the pink cardigan and the dress, the blue dress with small flowers on it. She wraps the red leopard-print scarf around her neck and arranges the scarlet beret just so. She smiles at me because I'm smiling at her. We kiss. We kiss at the table before leaving the restaurant. We kiss a sweet kiss. We kiss a soft kiss. We kiss a kiss of a knowing we're being watched kiss. We kiss the wrong kiss.

Outside it's cleared up a bit. The drizzle has lifted, for the moment, and the early afternoon in and around the cathedral is opening out. Open-top tour buses pass and I wonder as I always do how many photographs around the world have I appeared in because I happen to walk past tourists? Are we in a photograph today? Will a couple in Omaha or a retiree in Osaka pull up a slide show to show their friends sometime soon? Will they look at the cathedral and smile remembering their trip? Will they notice the couple walking by looking the other way?

Time is getting on.

I take her hand as we pass the cathedral again going back towards the Tube. We pass the archway of Temple Bar and she tells me she always feels like she's in *Great Expectations* every time she passes under it. Is she Pip? No. She's done all this herself. Is she Miss Havisham? No. Not her. No. Is she Estella? Is she? No. She creates herself and she creates her own version of the story. Her novel. I can see her though. I can see her passing here, passing Pip and Estella. I can see her passing here before. I can see her here passing after. I can see her here skipping past on her dancer's feet as the sirens ring and the searchlights scour the clouds. I can see her passing here, the schoolteacher, still clutching her ration book with her pink cardigan buttoned up over her blue dress with the small yellow flowers.

We pass by the arch and it's here. It's here. It's here in the shadow of the cathedral, here passing the archway, here under the leaden sky waiting to empty again. Here that I should kiss her. Here. Here I should kiss her properly. Holding her hand I should stop and kiss her. Here I should take her face in my hands, feeling the wool of the beret pulled down over her ears because of the chill and the damp and I should kiss her. Kiss her properly. But I don't.

Time is getting on. Time.

We're going the same way on the Tube. I'm getting out first. Time. Time. Feel the time like the clicking along the rails. Feel the time like the darkness and the light passing through the stations.

She asks if I'll put her in a story. I tell her she's my muse. I tell her she's my muse and I'll put her in a story. I tell her she's my muse as we pass from the darkness into the light of another station and she laughs. I tell her I'll call her Jane in my story. In my stories. And the time is running out. She wants to read more by me and the time is running out. Time running out and there's more I want to say. Time running out and I want to fit in all the words I couldn't fit in earlier in the restaurant near the cathedral. Time running out. We're almost ready to pull out of another station and she tells me I'll miss my stop and time is running out. I hug her again. I hold her again. I kiss her again but the time has run out. This is my stop. The time has run out. I'm only getting out here because I want to see if I can pick up a fucking CD I'm after but the time has run out. She laughs and jokingly pushes me away to make sure I get out at the right stop and the time has run out.

Walking towards the exit the train passes me by. I see her. I see her turned around, kneeling up on the seat of the train waving to me through the window. I see her kneeling up on the seat of the train in her navy blue coat and her red leopard-print scarf and her scarlet beret that I should have been feeling in my hands as I kiss her and I see her smiling at me and laughing and waving. I see her bright red lips and her sharp white teeth smile at me through the grime of the carriage window and the train passes down the tunnel and out of sight. Time. Time has run out, my time has run out. I walk towards the escalator and out onto the street. She carries on in the train.

Is she going back to Mount Helicon or is it Ealing Broadway?

Route not found

I fall in love. I never do.
I wave my hand and blur the world,
say: Tell me everything,
but do it slowly,
    slowly,
        so we still have things to tell
        when we are old.

Chase nostalgia round a cereal bowl,
for things we never even had,
for things that haven't happened,
yet: children in a swimming pool;
families with ice cream, side-by-side
on benches; a patrol boat putters past;
a group on a porch for a photo laughs;
there are ducks, being ducks.

I hide my keys so I won't throw them in the river.
I wouldn't, but worry I will.
Tell me, do you know how that is?

You said, am I hurting you?
And I should have said, not yet.

Now the wind flaps the flags too hard;
the group laughs too loud;
the children in the pool after dark
are too much. Now everything has turned,
too: You took a can opener to my heart,
see? Now I feel everything.

Things always end before they start.
I have no practice at the middle.
So I beg you:
tell me everything,
    but hurry,
    hurry

Molia Dumbleton

To the guy who tweeted,
Stop calling crap that ain't poems poems

It didn't even want to be a poem.

All it was was a topless jug
tied to the rudder of a sailboat
that could still make it to the other side
if the wind was good enough,
but only if one person steered
and the other just kept on bailing.

It was only ever a care-worn cap
hot-glued to a stake at the graveyard,
because *that* did more to make you
think of the *real* old head,
the one that was gone now, dead,
than a headstone ever did.

The whole thing to begin with
was nothing more than burnt-blue skin,
lovers' brands, committed to,
long before the last love's skin had
even finished smoking. This crap
didn't set out to be a poem, see.

It didn't want to be a goddamn thing.
It was just that the hollowness
Of something once full
Crooked its finger.
Made it play at something it wasn't.

Molia Dumbleton

Being the other girl

A girl writes to her lover
as he catches my eye.
'Wanna dance?' I say,
and he winks at me.

As he catches my eye
she brushes her teeth,
and he winks at me.
'Welcome,' I say.

She brushes her teeth
as her lover walks through my door.
'Welcome,' I say.
He smiles at me.

As her lover walks through my door
she sleeps in her bed.
He smiles at me.
'Kiss me,' I say.

She sleeps in her bed
as her lover takes off my bra.
'Kiss me,' I say.
Our lips are touching.

As her lover takes off my bra,
she dreams about him.
Our lips are touching,
and I touch his chest.

She dreams about him
as he walks out my door.
And I touch his chest.
'See you around,' he says.

As he walks out my door,
he catches my eye.
'See you around,' he says
and he winks at me.

Synne Johnsson

Caught in the Blue Beat

Emer Rogers

It is partly the estuary's fault that it's taking Grace this long to find a flatmate. It bullies the beaches down the coast so that new blood stops in town purely for petrol and a piss. Mostly though, it is because Grace is looking for more than just a flatmate, she wants one with a glut of off-the-rack mates, ready to sit out back in her yard, inhaling empty days and full cans.

Her flat, which she previously shared with Ma, is the downstairs of a tarnished two-tone green house in a row that tiptoes down the hill to the quay wall. Grace, paddling through her twenties, looks good; she's mastered sexily-messily hair from a YouTube video and her stomach, usually on display, still has the even sweep of a virgin dune.

She is up early, before eleven, because of the humidity, and she has narrowed the day down to Tuesday. Braless and with her feet on the sill of the sitting-room's shallow bay window, she wallows in Ma's old armchair, wiping away underboob sweat with the rump of her thumb at the same rate you'd apply a sleeve to a dripping nose. She watches two seagulls sink through the thick air, down the hill towards the pullulating stench of the ebbing tide.

It is then that Grace sees them.

Teenagers, five of them, all inexperienced in spending their empty days, have come to sit on the quay wall. With her heels still resting on the sill their distant figures trek across the tops of her toes. Look at them, she thinks, staring out across the estuary's sucking mire and festering about how different their lives would be if it were all sand.

Grace and her boobs jog out of step down the hill towards them. And by noon she is drinking own-brand beer in Ma's old bed with a boy called Tyler, who's just turned eighteen (he provided his provisional). Thundery clouds smother in, turning the light green-grey which accentuates the grime that creeps around the bedroom like a conquering ivy.

'I really should exercise more,' the words sail out of her mouth on exhaled smoke.

'You're still tight where I need it.' His soft lines have yet to harden.

Their limbs have twisted the sheet about them, so that a cotton grey whirlpool is circling a drain beneath her arse. The walls crowd the bed, as if feeling the swirling pull, and the smell stirred by their movement is fishy like it is all becoming too much for the drain. She doesn't think she was his first. He's only a young lad she tells herself, to quash the feeling she is being seen by a man used to making the best of bad. Ditching his can onto an ossified sock on the floor he asks, 'You got anything else?'

'I need my book,' she says, disappointed he hadn't brought anything.

'Why?'

'His phone'll be off now.'

Crouching on the mattress like a summoning shaman she flings the abused hardback up at the ceiling. Tyler shakes white flecks from his slick-back, toppling the long strands overboard into his undercut. A door slams, then another—her front door—and when the heavy feet pause, Grace, stepping into her knickers, guides them, 'Vinnie, in here.'

With his fly just buttoned Grace watches Tyler take in the exposed abs stepping through the door; ridges like the sandy seabed itself. Heading towards forty, Vinnie has begun wet-shaving his bony skull and face daily; it suits him, he looks invulnerable as if he's come back here on holiday for the craic, despite having died. The right side of his face is covered with raw meat, a vac-packed frozen steak.

'Sparring?' Grace asks.

'Sinuses. And I've nothing for ya, G.'

Standing on the bed she is his height and with feline proclivity slinks onto his forearm that hangs ready for her like a swing.

'Don't look at me like that, I told ya, not while I'm getting me creds. Who is he?' Vinnie nods at Tyler who replies from the far side of the bed with his name.

'And your mammy, boyo?'

'Sharon Mac.'

'No way, the granny in her thirties? The Whole in One?'

Grace flicks Vinnie's earlobe as if to change the conversation's channel.

'Tyler, Vinnie's a PT, a personal train—'

'Jesus, G, how old?' Vinnie asks.

'It's okay, I checked. Any canny-cans left?'

'No beer m'dear. Switch to mouthwash.'

Tyler puts on his runners, keeping his eyes on the size of Vinnie's feet in the gap under the bed.

'To drink like?' she asks.

'To rinse. Bang off of you.'

'I've got to go,' Tyler says.

'Hang on, so you've viewed the room…' Grace makes eye contact with him, 'And?'

'He live here too?' Tyler throws an eye at Vinnie.

'In the flat upstairs, just him, his mam is long gone, like my ma… well, my ma is not so long gone, she actually died—'

'You gonna take it or what?' Vinnie takes over while Grace goes off remembering the moment they popped her dead ma out of her armchair like a conker ripe from its shell.

'How much?'

'Two weeks up front, 120,' Vinnie says.

'Bit much…'

'Grand so, fix your fringe, Swifty, and piss off.'

'Vin, his name is Tyler not Taylor,' Grace says.

'G, you just said the same name twice.'

'No, one's with a Y,' she tries again.

'They both have a Y,' Vinnie says.

'I mean just a Y.'

'WIO always did have notions, Tyler for fuck sake like.'

'Fuck it, fine, 120,' Tyler says sitting back on the bed.

'WIO stands for Whole—' Vinnie stops as Grace hops from his arm saying, 'So, Tyler, you'll bring your friends over then?'

'Why? More rooms for them to view, have ya?

'To hang out, out the back like.' Grace pats Vinnie's advancing chest, his skull cocked at the boy's tone. 'You know with some cans, maybe do a little partying.'

'Yeah, whatever, I'll bring the 120 tomorrow night,' Tyler says passing Vinnie, who catches his wrist and slaps the steak into his hand. 'For your Mammy, I never bought her dinner first.'

*

Twenty-four hours later, Grace balances her groceries—noodle nests, soy sauce, fish fingers and a six-pack—on the withering compost mound that is her kitchen table.

On the way home she stepped in setting concrete. Shielded by a blue tarp the six feet of new footpath had looked perfect. The crinkled lines across it were like puckered wrinkles, calling out to be rubbed onto a crisp page with a thick red crayon, but she settled for pushing her foot down through its skin, sinking deeper than she planned when that woman appeared; the one Grace liked to think she'd look like if she had a job. The woman stared at Grace, not through or even at her, but more as if Grace was her reflection; like her worst angle revealed in a rippling shop window. A gull squawked as the woman hoisted her boobs by her bra straps, rallying her posture, and Grace fled the concrete and the feeling that the woman was about to flap wings and try to smash through the offending reflection.

She stands at the sink facing the window that frames the concrete wall and wire-fencing that has become her DIY prison yard. Outside Vinnie is doing burpees and his skull glistens each time he jumps into a sliver of sunlight.

Grace doesn't see Vinnie or the yard today, her gaze never gets through the pane, searching for a reflection not visible. Kicking off her flip-flop she grabs the dishcloth from over the neck of the tap and begins wiping her hoofed-back foot.

'Did ya call into Fang?' Vinnie has come inside to stretch his calf, leaning with his palms flat against the wonky fridge.

'What?' Grace asks.

'Fang?'

'Mm?'

'Prawn crackers?' Thigh flexed, Vinnie winces.

'Mmm-hmm.'

'What's wrong with your foot?'

'Nothing,' she says, still rotating her head in front of the window in search of her worst angle. Fang had also looked at her funny today, funnier than usual. Grace always feels on display for Fang and her changeable eyeballs. Her sockets are like peep holes where visiting sets of eyes come to gawk in at this strange thing, Grace in her zoo town. But Fang laughs at all Grace's jokes, and says things like, *You crack me up, my ace Grace*—which is enough to keep Grace going back.

Fang seems to have stayed the same age all Grace's life. She runs a takeaway; a hole-in-the-wall job the same colour as her sweet and sour while upstairs her studio flat smells of cooked cockle shells and steaming salt-water. She was a sort of dinner-lady to Grace, providing her meals without questions on schooldays when Ma's paranoia made her housebound. Ma concocted all kinds of stories, as Vinnie called them, but to Grace, Ma was just lying, sitting in her chair making up her own versions of events. And none of her versions were helpful. Fang and Vinnie were the only ones who came to Ma's funeral, and now most mornings Fang drinks tea while Grace eats prawn crackers for breakfast; the crackers dissolve in the dip, like Jesus on your tongue.

After today's breakfast though, Grace is unsure if she can ever return. She made an off-limits joke about the similarity between Fang and her mongrel: the two of them shuffling around, toenails clicking on the floorboards, with their Labrador-size heads on stout Corgi bodies. She only said it because of the postcard, the new one of a Chinese dragon pinned to Fang's fridge; it had become the third big head on a small body in the flat, and simply too much for Grace not to mention, lubed as she was on prawn crackers and compliments.

'Right, so you're a one-shoe pony now?' Vinnie asks.

She looks at his head, 'Yeah well a pirate called and he wants you to… to get back to work on the Jolly Roger.'

'What are ya on about, G?'

'It's a joke, your head is all bony, everyone thinks so.'

'I do have good structure… who's everyone?'

Grace pinches the prick in her finger, encouraging any last drop of blood. Fang had let her play with her lancet again. Grace is always encouraged by the sight of the red globule. It's confirmation that she is made of the same stuff as everyone else. Lately she has become perturbed about her eggs. Fang says hundreds of eggs are lost every month, but Grace isn't even sure she releases them, only sure that by now she should have surely seen one. Google did not have an answer to How do I see my eggs? so she has continued to look for clues in sitcoms where women demand sex from their busy husbands by saying, 'I'm ovulating. Come home.'

'Gracie?… G, stop poking your finger. I'm gonna bring the bench press out back yeah, just need something for the rain,' Vinnie says as he sits down on a kitchen chair.

'You're going to traipse clients through my kitchen?'

'Yeah, didn't think you'd mind, you drag enough fellas through here.'

She throws the dishcloth at him.

'But seriously if I'm bringing clients down we'll have to clean the place. Get rid of all the junk. The smell.'

'It's not that bad.'

'Think of it this way, G, you know on TV when the police go into a house because the neighbours are complaining about a smell?'

She takes the dishcloth from his hand and begins wiping her foot again.

'Do you really think they'd send someone to investigate like, if I died?'

He frowns at her, 'So one flip-flop just flipped right off then?'

'Just leave it will ya?' she says and takes a swig of soy sauce. She believes it masks the ash on her breath.

'Who's the beer for?' Vinnie asks.

'Tyler.'

'Good lay was he, like the Mammy? You can't teach it—it's in the genes, like being good at footie, or growing muscle, it's all predetermined like. But he's not actually moving in, is he?'

'Vinnie, don't start.'

'With the last one you let stay, you were a protester. We were making placards out the back like a sweatshop, and before that more games. He'll be the sixth flatmate in less than a year, G.' Grace opens her mouth to object, but Vinnie points the index at her. 'And now you're a schoolgirl for this one?'

'Vin, he's not a kid, and he's not like the others, all he needs from me is a place to stay. Sharon kicked him out, on moving her fella in. Look, it's just a room, Vin.'

'But, see, it's not just a room you're renting out, it's more like… it's yourself. That's exactly it, G, you can't keep renting yourself out along with the room. There won't be any of you left.'

'So what if I like having people around? When we were younger, people were always here, having parties for days, remember?'

'I do, kiddo, but I just don't like seeing you twist yourself for guys.'

She shrugs. 'This is what I want.'

He looks at her. 'Okay, but remember, no games. I'm not playing.'

Grace goes back to the sink.

'It was me, by the way, that came up with the Whole in One,' he says.

'Funny.' Grace holds the dishcloth around the tap like a hood, and Vinnie wraps his arms around her until she gives in to his gentle force and leans back into his sweaty chest. He whispers into her messy hair, 'But not nearly as funny as *my ace Grace*.'

Later that night, when it is as dark as a summer's night can get, Grace lets Tyler in with his GAA gear bag, its busted zip leaking a caseless pillow. She unfurls his limp fivers and tens, two of which are sterling, but she gives him a key and a can anyway. He says nothing as he shuts his bedroom door. Across the hallway in the kitchen she drinks three cans and leaves four voicemails for Vinnie—or it may have been four cans and three calls—and witnesses the blue fairy lights strung along the window lose a turf war to the rising light.

Tyler's room is darker and beside a sleeping Tyler she strips to her tank top and knickers, lifts the duvet and puts her head in his armpit and matches his breathing. Bored, she tries to count seagulls on the street based on their squawks.

Two, no three, no only two. Then she hears the front door open.

'Morning, Grace,' Vinnie shouts in, shaking his head as he turns into the kitchen. Her leap from the bed is followed by Tyler's roar; she elbowed his balls on take-off.

There is a clatter and a bang in the kitchen.

'He's just cleaning,' explains Grace.

'Time?' Tyler asks still squinting.

'Nearly six.'

'Morning like?'

'Mmm-hmm, sooooo when do you think we should have your house-warming party?'

He pulls the pillow, still caseless, across his face.

'Tyler?... Will you ring your mates then?' She slides his phone up to his chin.

'Anyone want breakfast? Steak, yeah?' Vinnie hollers in.

'No Vin,' Grace hollers back as Tyler mouths *fuck off*.

'Tyler, give him a chance, you guys have a lot in common, his Ma was...'

'What? A whore? A slut.' Tyler belches out the words from under the pillow. She kisses his velutinous chest.

'I was gonna say that she was young when she had him... So was mine actually.'

He fish-hops away from her and mutters something into the pillow which she hears as, 'Yeah, well, her nickname affect you?'

The Drone—it had affected her. Ma had got the nickname because of Grace. While watching telly in Vinnie's flat, Grace said, 'Guess what she said today, Vin? Calls me over to her bloody chair and goes—*God didn't make it obvious, Grace, and that was the only gift he gave woman*—Jesus, this is her motherly advice on orgasms like.'

Vinnie muted mangled cars on a desert road and pulled her across the sofa into his chest, 'G, your Ma is like a drone, she is high in the sky then she opens her mouth and fires down a bombshell completely off fucking target.'

Grace straddles Tyler without warning. He shoves her off.

'Christ, would ya stop.'

She sits wounded on the bed, flat on her arse, 'We'll chat about it later so.'

'Jesus' is audible from under the pillow so she throws it on the floor, 'That not suit, Tyler?'

He will not look at her, swiping open his phone instead. She watches his thumb orchestrate the information before his eyes: up, down, over and back.

'Tyler, look at me, can't you see I'm talking to ya?'

He laughs at a shouty GIF. This isn't childish, he has never been a child, he could live here happily and ignore her with authority. He would know how to do that. He would know all about eggs too. Snatching his phone she asks, 'Tyler you know on TV when women demand…'

'Christ, do you think I'll bring mates here to see another old wan and her fucking john.'

He continues to stare at the hand where his phone had been. Like a friendly pebble in her pocket she fingers—round and round—the thought of Tyler and his mates, out back having cans.

'Grace? You there?'

She tosses his phone up in the air and when it lands on the mattress beside him she has a lie ready, 'Vinnie doesn't pay me anymore.'

'For what?'

'The same things your Mam does.'

That evening she watches Tyler walk down the hill to his mates. They should be sitting in her yard not on the quay wall. She doesn't enjoy playing Vinnie but she needs him hostile to the boy.

She tells him Tyler has left her short on rent.

'Text him to come here now,' is Vinnie's reply.

They never usually sit in the kitchen, but it feels like the only place to wait for Tyler—on kitchen chairs dragged away from the composting table. Vinnie yabbers on about the blue tarp he'd stolen to rainproof the yard while Grace watches a seagull soar in and out of the window's range, squawking at a beeping bin lorry. Its belly glows blood orange from the setting sun.

'Why doesn't he just fly to the beach?' she asks.

'Sure this is what he knows,' Vinnie tells her.

Grace has forgotten about her ciggy in the scallop shell. It continues to burn, holding its flaky shape, waiting for a touch to blow it apart. At midnight Tyler's head finally crowns through the door and the three of them pause and look to each other.

'Busy?' Vinnie asks.

'No,' Tyler says. Leaning against the sink, he farts with an ease beyond his years.

'G texted you a while ago.' Vinnie sits back, open-legged with his hands a composed V at his groin.

'Didn't realise I was being timed.' He susses along the worktop like a dog let loose in new surroundings.

'About the rent…' Vinnie says.

'I rent from her,' Tyler interrupts.

'Well, it's between the three of us now.'

'I've paid,' Tyler says.

'In full?'

'Grace?' Tyler asks, but Grace bites her lips, she has to for the sake of the parties, the cans, the mates, the empty days out back.

'Leave her, you've upset her enough,' Vinnie says.

Tyler hoists up the yoke of his jeans back onto his waist. 'I upset her? Seriously Grace, you're saying nothing?'

She spins away from him on the seat cushion, tugging loose its strings.

'Okay, Vinnie, what about you not paying? No surprise like, you stiffed the mother as well like.'

'I stiffed yer Mammy for sure, boy, but I left her cash like everyone else in her arse crack, but what are ya on about with G?'

'Well, G told me you stopped paying her, a couple of months now.'

'Paying for what?'

'I didn't ask for specifics.'

'For what boyo?'

'Sex. You stopped paying her for sex.'

Vinnie's attention moves solely to Grace. The blue fairy lights give the kitchen an urgent feel, as if it is caught in the blue beat of a circling siren. Help lost on its way. She takes a deep breath, swallowing some saved tear-drips to make a crackle in her throat.

'Tyler, you need to leave, mate,' Vinnie says, still looking at Grace.

'What?' Tyler says.

'Tyler, trust me, get fucking gone. Grace, I'm done with this, I'm done…' Vinnie kicks the back door open and stands out on the step; a moth flutters in, stops and flies straight back out over his head again.

'You swore you'd stop the lying after the protester.' He disappears out into the unlit yard.

'Grace, it doesn't have to be like this,' Tyler grabs Grace's arm. Vinnie roars in from the dark, and Grace feels Tyler jump and chances a look up at him but Vinnie is back in the doorway. 'I see ya, Gracie, biting back a smile at this poor fucker, your hero boy. Thinks he's seen this all before with the WIO.' He leans against the fridge; palms flat, head bent like he's stretching. 'Gracie are you sure this is what you want?'

She remains rigid in the chair, and when her tears shift, reflex takes him the three strides to Tyler: 'Get gone.'

'It's our flat. You go,' Tyler says, lining himself up for the hit.

Vinnie's fist finds bone under his pudgy cheek and makes a fleshy divot. This wasn't Tyler's first either, Grace thinks as he hums a hymn of curses with his arse backed up against the sink.

'Ready to go now?' Vinnie takes one of the vac-pack steaks from the freezer to cover his knuckles.

'I have nowhere to go,' Tyler says.

'Then I'm sorry for ya, boy, you haven't a clue,' Vinnie says throwing him the dishcloth from over the tap for the blood. They stand still in the blue light and listen to the fridge's whirring. 'We could have just had steak and noodles,' Vinnie says looking up at her from his knuckle.

'Forget him, Grace, the lads are coming over now.' Tyler's phone lights up his face. Grace winks at Vinnie, but he just moves on with his closing lines.

'Enjoy your backup party, Swifty. FYI, if they're your size, you'll need at least three of ye.' Vinnie flicks up his T-shirt sleeve and flexes his bicep. He leans over Grace, as Tyler continues texting, and whispers into her hair: 'You probably should have cried when I hit him, G.'

She leans back to fit into his chest but he's at the door, shaking his head, 'Well played, m'dear, I'm done.'

Grace sits in Ma's armchair waiting for the navy night to melt to blue. With her head against the velvety cushion her heart thumps in her ears like the beats of a distant party. She closes her eyes and tries to follow the beats to it.

'Grace, you want a can?' Tyler shouts in through the serving hatch.

'He's a gull.'

'What?'

'He'll be back down.'

'Don't worry, the lads will be here soon.'

'Are there enough canny-cans?' she asks as she tries to catch her reflection in the bay window, of her worst angle, any angle. Tyler pokes his head through the hatch, 'The lads are bringing enough. Enough. For. Days.'

'The yard is what he knows.' She stays staring at her reflection but the tip-toeing houses keep breaking through. A gull fades in and out. A bald gull. No feathers, a skull head. She is smiling.

'Ah, that's better. They all can't wait to see the famous Grace.' Tyler is walking over to Ma's armchair, his arm stretched out to her with a can.

'Will they though?' she asks still staring at the windowpane.

The flat, the street, the tide are all quiet. Two mates with cans. Almost there.

'A party,' she says.

'Just what ya need, G,' Tyler says, ignoring her.

A Lesson in Needlework

A tumbler of bourbon, some pills.
Beethoven in the background.

You are out somewhere.
The clock is driving itself insane,
going round in circles.

Two more pills, another glass.
A man is yelling on the street—
I can't understand what is happening.

A tumbler of bourbon, some more pills.
There is blackness so engrossing
I feel there is no way back.

There are strange men yelling in the vastness
of our living room.

There is a snake in my throat
pumping black venom.

My head over the bathtub
vomiting the venom out.

There are strange men yelling
about the hospital, there is a tug of war
between you and me and the strange men yelling—

something about their jobs and liability.

There is silence.
There is glass over the floor.

You are walking me around the vastness of our living room,
tenderly.

I can't understand what is happening.

You are there, trying to understand
what I myself can't comprehend,
tenderly.

There is the tiger beating
out from the centre of my chest.
It beats and beats and will not stop.

The clock is driving itself insane,
going round in circles

and despair is a lesson in needlework,
a black-stitched pattern,
endlessly weaving both of us into it.

Lorcán Black

Adeline

At noon in the deadpan February sun,
I run into my neighbour, Adeline—
an actress who once fell unconscious

at our fondue dinner, fainting
in the garden from the staggering
smell of melted cheese. She starts

unsnapping the buttons of her goose down
coat. She opens it like stage curtains
to reveal the planet she carries, and laughs

excitedly as if she were suddenly swimming,
naked. Her poinsettia hair has thickened
into a flaming fern. My laugh joins hers

as the tight ellipses of her stomach bumps mine.
Any moment now, her body—so satisfyingly round—
might rise into space and not come down.

Stephanie Papa

Holiday

Freshly divorced, my uncle leans back as he swirls a Chablis,
Smells dead lobster tucked in ice at the fishery,
Limp like marionettes, and hears a boy shriek as he lets a balloon go.
My father's younger brother takes a discreet dose of our waitress,
His bachelor vision engrossed in the loose gap of her shirt
As she reaches to place a basket of bread on our table.
Wrinkles pleat around his eyes like a child's drawing of a sun,
And he utters what seem like his first ever words:
'I think a few girls have been looking at me,' he says.
I don't tell him that in Paris, everyone looks at each other.
His kinked Italian nose eagles towards his wine glass,
And some inner force urges more words forth:
'I like these little streets,' he says, 'I like all these little streets.'
My uncle has become an almost happy man.

Stephanie Papa

Syzygy

You sleep on my chest,
                hands splayed like a sunset
        on muslin clouds after a
storm of tears, the moon
        of your mouth pulling
                the tide of my milk
                        the sound of the ocean
                                in every breath.

Aoife Lyall

Inge

Nora Pyne

Inge's youngest child died during the night, quietly. That left four children still living, and another, beside this one now, dead.

Inge's first died of a fever years earlier on the boat from Norway. The sailors buried her mid-Atlantic, a tiny shrouded body dropped into the lapping water. Inge heard the splash as a slap: a holding to account of her failings. She stood alone, still and silent at the railing while the pastor and informal congregation of passengers finished their last prayer. The pastor shook her hand. 'Take comfort,' he said. 'Everything is God's will.' Inge went below and lay motionless in her berth until the next morning, her back turned against the noise of all the languages and lives in the shared married and family third-class cabin. The pastor's voice echoed in her mind: 'God has his reasons.'

Inge's second child was her first born in Canada: a girl name Hilde, now grown to a woman. Hilde lived in town and had no interest in the farm. Wilbur was third and he was away being a soldier. Inge worried every day for having him so far away. Then came the twins, Einar and Karl, who were asleep in the next room, pressed tight together, huddled and warm under thick blankets on an achingly cold February prairie winter morning. That made six; six children in total.

The birth of the baby dead only a few hours, the last child, had come as a surprise. Inge thought there would be no more. It was twenty-five years from her first and she and her husband were more old now than they were young. Only a few months earlier Inge had glanced up while ironing Sunday shirts and saw an unexpected face in the little mirror tacked next to the kitchen stove; she was startled by the grey, haggard woman looking back. Inge thought it was her mother, long gone many years.

This was why it didn't occur to Inge she was pregnant, even though she had been many times before. Mary MacRennie, from the farm one over, eyed her up and down on a Friday afternoon. They were making soap in Mary's kitchen with lye from the ash barrel and strained fat from saved drippings.

'Inge?' she asked, stirring the heating pots and seeing the new fullness of her friend's body. 'Have you got yourself again in a family way?'

Inge looked so shocked Mary laughed.

'You're not are you?' Mary said. 'Oh my, Inge, you are.'

Inge told Edmund that night she was pregnant again. He was happy, but he knew she was not.

Inge and Mary made the soap before Christmas, and it was only a Saturday early in May that the twins were sent running to get Mrs MacRennie. They chased each other across the yard, past the henhouse and through a windbreak of quaking aspen to the next farm. The boys were always in motion. In the few photographs that still exist of that time, from picnics or barn raisings when the whole town came out, at least one of the twins is just a blur, unable to stand still even for the few seconds of an open shutter. Mary was rolling out a pie crust when they rushed through her kitchen door.

'Come back to yourselves boys,' she said, smiling.

Karl and Einar were eleven. They wanted a new baby, but in the same way they liked it when the cows calved in the spring.

Mary packed up a few things in a small net bag. She sent Karl out to the fields to tell her husband where she had gone and walked to Inge's with Einar.

'Now,' she asked him, 'what have you been thinking about names? Horseshoe, or maybe Apple Pie?'

Einar reached for Mary's hand, even though he was big now.

Inge had already taken the good sheets off the bed. She'd laid down an old flannel blanket over a large piece of cloth Edmund had waterproofed the month before, brushed with boiled linseed oil. Mary sent Edmund back to work, leaving the women to their own.

'We'll keep Einar handy,' she said, 'in case of needing him to get you.'

Edmund stopped by the barn on his way, making sure the horse was fed and watered, and the saddle ready. Mary put the boy to cutting kindling outside the kitchen door.

'Now Inge,' said Mary, once Edmund and Einar had left them alone. 'All the babies you've had already, this one's going to slip out. We'll be having a cup of tea in an hour. Let's see how far along you are.'

She was right, and Inge pushed the small body from her own a few minutes later, the pain so familiar she didn't need any unnecessary crying from the surprise of it. Mary helped guide the baby out directly onto the soft flannel. Inge looked down at the bloody mewling infant between her spattered legs. She sighed. Inge always thought the same thing when her children were born, even when she tried to not think it: of dressing rabbits in the kitchen, and the raw, skinned bodies haphazardly splayed in the red-stained, white enamel sink, helpless and so vulnerable.

'She's gorgeous!' Mary said.

Inge took a deep breath, feeling her lungs open into parts of her body that had been borrowed the last few months. The baby was a girl, with all her fingers and toes, and a strong cry. Mary lifted her to Inge's arms. The baby instinctively turned her head, rooting, and latched at Inge's breast, her little mouth a perfect pursed seal, suckling a nipple turned the colour of livid plum since the last weeks of pregnancy.

Mary had a jug of warm water for washing ready and a basket of folded clean rags. She went to the kitchen for the teapot, returning with two cups of tea laced sweet with sugar, almost like it was any other afternoon the past twenty years, except for the tiny new person in the crook of Inge's arm. Inge and Mary's ritual, the baby then the tea, had started when Hilde was born twenty-two years earlier and continued through the nine deliveries they'd had between them since. 'There's nothing better than that first cup after you've got a new baby out,' said Mary, 'just to catch your breath.' She passed the biscuits. 'Sláinte,' said Mary, raising her teacup.

Inge knew Mary was waiting; 'Skål,' she answered.

Mary dipped her biscuit in her tea. 'I just love a decent biscuit,' she said. 'Give me a Norwegian birth any day—good biscuits. Remember that Russian family? Sweet Jesus! What was that? Some hard mean thing not fit to dip into a cup of tea.'

Mary went on, talking for both of them: 'Brits, Scots, the Irish. The French, they're good. But not so much Yvette Proulx. Everything that woman made was burnt, God rest her.'

Mary crossed herself and drank her tea. Inge closed her eyes, just for a minute, sitting on the bloodied oilcloth nursing the baby, naked except for an unbuttoned chemise for modesty, holding the teacup in her free hand. She was sure the fatigue must be showing on her face already, working its way from deep inside her. After all these years living next to each other, Inge knew that having children was harder for her that it seemed to be for Mary, who thrived with each new baby. Inge never talked about it, and Mary never pried, not too much; the MacRennies and Sorensons were good neighbours, which is a blessing on prairie homesteads, and both families knew it. When Inge opened her eyes, Mary was watching her, silently mouthing the final words of a prayer.

'Right,' Mary said, brushing crumbs off her skirt, 'just one more biscuit and we'll get it all tidied up.'

The baby was named Magda, after Edmund's mother, and they had her baptised a week later at the Lutheran church in town. After the service, everyone gathered in the church hall to catch up on news of cows and grain prices and letters from those away. The women passed around plates of butter cookies and poured boiled coffee. Inge, old enough to be Magda's grandmother, wished they could just leave and go home. She asked Hilde to hold the baby.

'She looks better with you,' Inge said, when Magda was in Hilde's arms. 'You'll have a baby of your own soon, four years married.'

'Three,' said Hilde.

Inge worked a loose thread in the sleeve of her dress and pulled it free, smoothing away imaginary wrinkles. They said nothing for a minute. Hilde watched her mother's hand ironing, elbow to wrist, then straightening cuffs.

'I'll add some fabric in the store's next order,' Hilde said, 'so you can make yourself a new dress when you have time.'

Inge looked at her dress. The cotton was good: a durable plain weave. The buttons came from an old shirt of one of the twins: Einar's, or maybe Karl's.

'This is fine for another year,' she said and her eyes flitted around the church hall. 'Is it not four years now?'

Hilde spoke to the baby: 'Only three.'

Inge fingered a button at her collar.

'Think of the cost, Hilde,' Inge said, pausing. 'No, there's no need wasting money when this is still serviceable. Better you save for your own baby. I'm sure it will happen soon.'

The pastor's wife offered them more coffee, working her way through the crowd.

After a minute Inge spoke into the silence: 'I hear you've got a woman coming in to do the laundry?'

Hilde adjusted the baby's bonnet. 'Yes,' she said. 'I have a woman coming in to do the laundry.'

Across the room, the men shook Edmund's hand, and one of them said something quietly so that they all laughed, Edmund included, and they clapped him on the back. Magda started to fuss.

The twins took to having a new baby in the house. They danced and aped at the cradle, trying to outdo each other making her laugh. Edmund played with Magda too, hiding his face behind his hands, then peeking out. He had played with all the children. Inge kept Magda clean and fed. She picked her up when she cried and rocked her in the rocking chair, patting her back. Inge waited for the blackness to descend over her, but this time, with this baby, it wasn't as quick to come.

Mary made a point of visiting Inge's kitchen every afternoon those first few weeks, taking her knitting or a bag of socks to darn. The baby was fine, but Inge could tell Mary wanted to make sure she had settled. There's a difference, Inge well understood, between taking care of a baby and caring for a baby.

On one of those afternoons in Inge's kitchen, Mary told Inge a story about her own boys, how years before they'd taken their sister's dress from the clothesline and put it on the dog.

'Ah well,' Mary had said, laughing, 'even then you can't help but love them.'

Inge looked surprised. Magda was napping in her arms.

'Do you love all your children?' Inge had asked.

It had never occurred to Inge that she needed to, or even that she was supposed to love them all. Edmund left for Canada while she was pregnant with the first child, the little girl who died during the Atlantic crossing. Inge had sent a telegram when the ship docked in Montreal so Edmund would know he had only one person to collect a week later. Her train finally pulled at the tiny Saskatchewan station after a week of forests and mountains, thick clouds of black flies and, for the last day and a half, broad, flat plains. The station was more a collection of wooden planks hammered together to make a short platform and a wind-buffeted shed for the stationmaster, who was also the grain agent. A box of peonies grew on the shed's one window ledge. The grain elevator stood tall next to the platform and two men were outside doing figures on a scrap of paper laid flat on the top of a barrel.

'Only you,' Edmund had said on the station platform, hesitating before taking her hands in his own.

'Yes,' she answered.

She was standing next to her steamer trunk. The train conductor had lowered it down from the baggage car.

'There's only me.'

She didn't know what else to say.

They had met each other two weeks before they married. His aunt knew her mother.

'The boy is a hard worker,' the aunt had said, sitting at Inge's parents' kitchen table, 'with a land grant in Canada. He has a full 160 acres all in his own name.'

The aunt's hands clasped her bag firmly on her lap.

'The Erikson boys write their parents the soil is good but there are very few women. My brother thinks he needs a wife before he goes, a local wife They want a girl who can make lutefisk; one who comes from a hard-working family.'

Mama nodded her head, calculating the cost of one less mouth to feed, with Papa sick. There was quiet in the kitchen. The aunt looked around, inspecting for dust, and could see none. She turned back to Mama, satisfied.

'Edmund's already arranged the plough and team of horses himself. It's only the wife he's needing. He's quiet, but he's a good boy.'

Mama offered Edmund's aunt a slice of apple cake to go with her cooling tea.

Inge was not asked her opinion, nor was Edmund. Inge's mother said she would be wise to be sensible. Edmund sailed a month later, expecting to save enough money to send for his new wife within two years. It was impractical he left her pregnant; that had surprised them both.

Two years later exactly, as a young woman standing on the train platform after the long journey from Norway, across the Atlantic and across Canada, how could Inge explain the time that had passed to her husband, him nearly a stranger to her: the iron tablets, the prescribed nature walks, the tonics? None of it made any difference to the suffocation she felt through her pregnancy and then afterwards, the dense fatigue and darkness that wrapped around her like a fog rolling up from the harbour, never lifting. She spent her nights awake, unable to sleep until dawn and her days had no sense of time passing. Inge didn't know what she was supposed to do with the small person who followed her every movement with big eyes and then, as months passed, held unsteadily to her skirts.

When the baby died on the ship, Inge felt no tears, though she wanted to be able to cry. At least she wanted to be able to do that. She knew she was disappointing the other mothers, women ready to come to her with cool compresses and soft words in all their different languages. She lay in her berth with her back to the cabin through the long day after the baby was buried in the dark sea. For hours, she willed herself not to roll over, or open her eyes, or ask for some water to drink, even though she was thirsty. She didn't think she deserved to be comforted. Inge felt the child's final convulsions before dying as a deserved reproach: eyes fluttering, unfocused; tiny spasming hands held up in supplication; body burning with heat; too weak even for a feeble cry. The miniature husk of a corpse left behind, visibly empty of soul, was tangible proof to Inge of her incompetence. She hadn't wished the baby ill will ever, but she'd felt the same towards her from the baby's first day of life to her last: uncertain, confused and at best, only pretending to be the child's mother. She had failed both the baby and Edmund. It wasn't an accident the child was taken: 'God has his reasons.'

On the train platform two weeks later, Inge had raised her face towards the grey sky. She felt a first few drops of rain land. How could she tell Edmund any of this? How could she tell him she hadn't been good enough to be the mother of his child, of her own child? She couldn't.

'Yes, only me,' she said

Her mind couldn't think of the right next words.

'No. You didn't, I mean, you—' said Edmund.

'It's going to rain,' Inge interrupted.

'Yes,' said Edmund, looking at the sky, 'it's the rainy time of year. But you—'

Inge couldn't let him forgive her that easily. That was what he was about to do.

'Your mother sent you socks,' she said. 'Blue with white stripes. They're very nice. We should go before the rain comes.'

It was many years before they spoke of it again.

A few months later, settling into her new life in Canada, Inge was pregnant again. Just as before, the tiredness came in pregnancy and lingered after Hilde was born. Inge felt like her body did the motions of living while her spirit was somewhere else, but it was familiar and she expected it, so she managed. Inge couldn't hide everything from Edmund, but she got from day to day.

Hilde stayed; she didn't die like her older sister.

'A bit away with the fairies,' Mary agreed about Hilde as she grew up, 'but isn't she so clever with her arrangements of flowers, and a pretty girl too.'

Inge pointed out dropped stitches in Hilde's knitting and unravelled socks to let Hilde start again. Hilde scorched collars when she ironed, which Inge said was confusing, considering the simplicity of the task.

'How do you ever expect to be—,' asked Inge, searching for the right word in English, 'to be practical?'

As she got older, Hilde grew even prettier. She wasn't smart, but she was clever. In the summer she was nineteen, a week after the annual church picnic at Macaw Lake, the widowed town storekeeper came to call on a Sunday afternoon. He asked to speak to Edmund, alone. Hilde, since then married three years, now stood behind the counter at the general store and ordered all the Ladies Goods and Sundries, which she arranged carefully in the shop window, as well as the seasonal displays of farm equipment and also baking supplies. Her windows received compliments from the salesmen and once, a special award from the Blue Ribbon Manufacturing Company in Winnipeg, displayed on the wall behind the cash register, next to notices about store credit. The lace at Hilde's cuffs and collar was now always store bought, often in a shade of pale pink.

After Hilde, Inge's next child was Wilbur. The pregnancy had been different from the first two. Edmund and Inge finally had time for their quiet version of courting in the years after they were married. Winters are long in Saskatchewan; they eventually had enough nights sitting together by the fire to be at ease. A young Jim MacRennie knocked at the door one evening, bringing over a new book Mary had just finished: *Tom Grogan* by Francis Hopkinson Smith.

'It's about a bold Irishwoman who takes over her husband's identity when he dies to carry on famously and support the family,' said Jim. 'Mary loved it.'

Edmund read aloud to Inge that winter while she knitted. They looked up English words they didn't know in the dictionary. The year after that, he read her *The Day's Work* by Rudyard Kipling, all short stories. She liked Edmund reading to her. The farm was doing well too; the harvests had been good. Edmund planted saplings next to the house, someday to bear apples and pears for his wife. Inge felt secure. She was content. She wrote her mother to say that yes, she was tired in the pregnancy, but not tired in the same way, and not tired as much.

Wilbur's birth in the early spring had been easy. When July and August winds baked the prairies, Inge bathed Wilbur on the covered front porch, keeping him cool, while Hilde played with her dolls. When there was no one to see her except Hilde and she was certain Edmund wasn't in the house, Inge would hold her son up to her face, close her eyes and breathe deeply the smell of his skin, especially at his neck. She couldn't explain why she did this and she couldn't think what the smell exactly was either, but there was warmth and the honey orange of a Chinook sunset, and the freshness of a new crop of wheat coming up, all mixed with something indescribably satisfying, and she couldn't believe she had never smelled it before.

Now he was twenty years old and Wilbur was in Europe. His last letter home was postmarked from Amiens, in France. Wilbur, Mary and Jim's oldest son Angus, and the other boys from Unity and the nearby farms were all part of the 1st Battalion, Canadian Mounted Rifles, Canadian Expeditionary Force. The schoolteacher in town had specially ordered *The Atlas of Western Europe* from the Department of Education catalogue. When new letters arrived, people visited Miss Monahan at the schoolhouse to search the atlas for postmarks.

Inge had not been able to hide the fear in her face when Wilbur and Angus came home after signing up, the boys triumphant and boisterous, filled with the bravado of adventure. She said there was no need for him to go when there was so much work on the farm, but Wilbur laughed and said they were Lutherans, not Mennonites or crazed naked Dukhobors protesting the war outside the legislative buildings and anyway, he and Angus would look out for each other. The boys had been away nearly two years now.

Inge and Edmund's twins were next, born when Hilde was eleven and Wilbur nine. Hilde claimed her brothers from the beginning as if they were her babies, fussing over their clothes and arranging their soft curly hair. Mary MacRennie told Hilde it was her extra important job, and that Hilde was to be a great girl with the twins and her younger brother Wilbur too. Inge had to stay in bed for nearly a month. She hadn't expected two babies and had hemorrhaged in delivery, then was ill with infection. On top of that, so sick sometimes she didn't know where or who she was, the dark emptiness had returned and wrapped around her in a stranglehold. The infection cleared after a few weeks, but she wept for hours and hours, day after day. Edmund spoke with Mary and Mary arranged to have a wet nurse, even though the eight dollars each month was a real strain.

Despite there being two of them, the twins had needed Inge less than any of the other children, and this made it easier. Einar proved to be good-natured and Karl not as much, but he tried. They both loved Hilde, and as they got older, the boys were happy to work on the farm with their father when they weren't in school.

Last came Magda, the unexpected baby, born that year, in May of 1916, delivered by Mary and followed by a cup of sweet tea. Yes, Inge was tired, but she was always tired. She worried, but Inge always worried. On the other hand, the farm and her family were well. Inge could only wait to see what would happen.

August that year was solid with unmoving heat. Inge rested in the afternoon shade of the front porch, Magda in her cradle. Edmund and the boys were at work in the barn. Inge rocked the cradle with her foot, fanning herself, sweat staining her dress in crescents under each arm. Magda babbled and chewed her hand.

That morning, Mary had run through the windbreak, all one hundred and eighty pounds of her, apron flapping, hair flying loose from her hairpins. She was waving a letter from her son Angus. Wilbur's letter would arrive a few days later. The newspaper headlines for the past month had been nothing but the Somme Offensive. Nearly every farm was waiting for a letter, and praying not to see the telegraph boy instead… *buried Jack McCabe and his cousin Frank, who died next to each other so we buried them same. Please tell McCabes it was quick and boys felt nothing. Frank had only received photo of new baby. Frank was proud and glad to see such a fine looking child. Say so to his wife. Do not worry yourselves as all others well. Wilbur here beside me, writing to the Sorensons. Thank you for chocolate and tobacco, which was greatly appreciated. Kiss everyone. Say to boys they need to help Daddy do my share of the work. Pray we see each other soon. With love, Angus.* On the porch that afternoon, thinking about the letter, Inge felt her breath come easier. She was sad for the McCabes; they were good people, but her son was alive on the date Angus put pen to paper.

At her feet, Magda smiled, or at least it seemed like she smiled. Inge was surprised: Magda, she had never noticed before, looked like Wilbur had as a baby. Magda's eyes focused on her mother and she reached out, touching Inge's mouth. Inge took Magda's hand away. Magda did it again. Inge pretended to nibble the baby's fingers and Magda squealed in delight.

Inge went inside and at the kitchen pump, filled a shallow basin with water. She brought the basin back, moving slowly through the hot air, and laid it down on the porch. Even the first pump water was warm. Inge undressed the baby, lowering her carefully. Inge smiled a second time when Magda kicked out to splash with her feet. They played, Inge gently bobbing the baby up and down, little waves rolling over Magda's stomach. When she finally picked Magda up out of the basin, Inge leaned her head down tentatively, then brushed her nose across the baby's skin to take a delicate inhale of Magda's neck before latching her to nurse.

After the harvest, with the weather still fine but cooling, Inge made herself a new Sunday dress. It was a dark shade of green from the length of poplin Hilde sent out to the farm. The note tucked inside said: *Mama, It's already paid for, so please use it for yourself. Hilde.* Edmund visited his daughter at the general store later in the week to collect a crate of canning jars. On a whim, he brought black velvet piping for the dress, choosing from the spools Hilde showed him. Hilde gave him a twist of hard candy for the twins: mixed root beer and butterscotch. Inge agreed that the trim at the cuffs added to the dress, and she kept to herself about the extra cost. She made Magda a little cape with the leftover material and velvet edging, even though Magda didn't need it.

The weather turned and the cold autumn winds started. Inge learned a few of Edmund's songs, the ones he had sung to the other children. She sang with Magda on her knee after everyone left for school or the barn. Inge took her out twice a day to feed the chickens, the baby's favourite thing to do. Mary MacRennie brought over a collection of Beatrix Potter books no one in her house was reading anymore.

'I'm saving them for grandchildren,' she said, 'but that's still a few years away. No harm Magda getting some use.'

Inge was awkward at first. She had to ask Mary the meaning of some of the very English words.

'What,' she asked, 'does kertyschoo mean and why does the rabbit not listen to his mother?'

Mary told her. Inge thought the books too fanciful, with dancing animals in waistcoats having feelings, cats hosting tea parties and sly foxes reading newspapers. Magda seemed to enjoy the sound of her mother's voice. Inge kept reading, and one night the twins decided they weren't too old they couldn't look at the pictures as well. Edmund listened from his chair by the fire.

At the church Christmas pageant that year, Inge enjoyed herself so much she managed to compliment Hilde's altar design without saying the wrong thing. She didn't need to go over her words in her head with regret, like the usual conversations with her older daughter. Inge held Magda in her arms the entire evening, even when Hilde offered to take her. Edmund whispered in Inge's ear as the twins delivered their lines as the Magi and she delighted him when she laughed. Everyone admired the baby's green cape with black velvet trim.

In February, the first big storm kept the boys home from school. The freezing cold set in and temperatures dropping to minus forty. On the morning Magda died, Karl and Einar were still asleep. Inge woke late, at six, with Edmund snoring beside her. The baby was in her crib. Inge stretched over to check. It was still too dark to see, but Inge was listening and there was nothing to hear.

The baby wasn't breathing. Inge stayed motionless for a long moment, and then another, until she was certain nothing was going to change. She got up silently, to not wake Edmund. She wrapped herself in her heavy wool shawl, then went downstairs to the kitchen. She could see her breath In the air. Inge stirred the embers in the stove, adding kindling and blowing softly until the fire caught. She dragged her rocking chair close, and went back upstairs for Magda, picking her up and making sure she was properly covered in her baby quilt. In the cold kitchen, Inge sat with the baby in her arms and rocked slowly.

There was no point in crying, Inge told herself, no point. Babies died all the time. At the Larson's farm, on the other side of the MacRennies', they lost one this way the year before, during an afternoon nap. At the Olafsons, they'd had a problem with their well and during the summer three of their children died. It happened. Inge continued rocking, pushing against the floor with her foot, slow and steady, the chair creaking back and forth. She adjusted Magda's blanket, tucking the edges to keep out draughts.

'Why did you not stay, my baby?' Inge whispered to Magda.

The wood in the fire hissed like it was slowly sucking in huge breaths and crackled loudly, a series of small explosions as the frozen water in its veins turned to steam. The sound echoed Inge back to the deck of the ship twenty-five years earlier, to the condemnation as the shrouded body of her first child fell from the ship, hit the ocean with a splash and disappeared into the water. She understood the answer she had been given: 'God has his reasons.'

Inge had let herself forget she didn't deserve to love her children. It wasn't for her to decide otherwise, just because this time she felt different. God was angered by her arrogance and selfishness, angered by her hubris. Inge's grief scourged across her face. It was the little cape to match her own dress that caused this; the cape with velvet trim was an act of arrogance God couldn't ignore. Inge rocked Magda and she cried and cried until all her tears were gone.

Later in the morning, Edmund and the twins made the tiny coffin at the kitchen table while Inge watched from the rocking chair, her eyes red. They lined it with an old white cotton pillowcase, worn thin with many washings. Hilde had done the edging embroidery when she was a girl, her Queen Anne stitch uneven. When the coffin was ready, Inge stood up. She gently placed her daughter inside, the scent of Magda's skin in her memory.

Inge had been thinking about God. She wouldn't taunt Him with a single tear more, afraid he might think she hadn't been punished enough. God would take another child, and then another, until she showed her acceptance of His will. Inge was afraid God would take Wilbur. She needed Wilbur to come home safely. She would show no more tears, no more indulgence in love. She would protect Wilbur from God.

Edmund fit the coffin lid over Magda. He put on his coat and picked the box up in his arms, the weight of his daughter light. Inge stood still beside the wood stove. He nodded at her, waiting to be sure Inge was ready for him to take Magda away. The porch door closed behind Edmund and he carried the coffin across the yard, the weak sun barely risen, bathing the farmyard in a pale anaemic light. The air outside was bitterly cold and Edmund's own tears, in this private place, froze on his eyelashes. The animals in the barn made their low, snorting noises. He put the coffin in a burlap sack and hung it over a high crossbeam, out of reach from wolves, foxes and especially the rats. The body would freeze. Edmund and the boys would have to wait for spring for the ground to thaw to dig a grave.

Inside the house, Inge went upstairs. She was still in her nightdress and shawl, and there were the day's chores to do. She had the bread to start. There were wood shavings from the coffin under the kitchen table to sweep up. Inge sat on the edge of her bed. Her breasts were leaking. Inge looked down at her veined bony hands, a record of all those years of hard work and she felt inescapably old. The dark heaviness started devouring all the air in the room as it came down around her.

The Soldier on Clare Island

Later we will picture U-boat torpedoes skeeting water,
shattering a ship's keel, rupturing its hull.
And imagine him flipped into the air, flopped
backwards, explosions splashing the various distances—
shards of hissing metal, limbs of men, bales,

boxes, bags and barrels enough to tide Noah's ark
over the deluge. And dream of fishes
weaving in and out of his wounds, slick as needles
threading stitches through mounds
of cloth draped across our nanas' thighs. In games

and quiet reflections he will live on, he will move
again—the dead soldier, ocean currents
spinning him towards us by trouser cuff or coat lapel,
sousing his ear, braiding seaweed in his hair.
But the day he arrives, nudging against the rocks,

all we are able to do is shrink to the reticence
our parents and neighbours wear as a way of life,
the set notions of dignity they expect
from us. He floats, so much a sodden garment
we are unsure at first whether there is a body or not.

A fisherman's hands gather him up
where we stoop, short-trousered, splay-toed. The sea
relinquishes its grip in surly rivulets emptying.
His face, sky-lit but dull, gives him away.
His uniform, once remarked on, seems no longer

to fit him. An Englishman—the grizzled heads nod—
he must be Protestant, so. Their words
perturb us out of our welling pity. No name found,
no place to send him home to, measures
taken for a decent burial, a graveyard of his own

beyond the shoulder of our Catholic cemetery.
War thunders elsewhere. Echoes reach us, 'dispatches'
from either side neutrally reported, and he,
a casualty spat by the long-drawn Battle of the Atlantic,
is considered part of the necessary detriment.

But if strafings we suffer seem slight by comparison,
storm and tidal swell still cut us off; we feel
the pang of infant deaths, of kinfolk exiled, of famine
remembered around smoky turf fires,
or forebears grieved as we stare at lazy-bed

residues of old potato ridges skeletally stretched.
Wonders happen regardless, nature
requiring only itself. Birds sing the rinsed air and light,
spiders' webs glisten on the spars of gates,
tadpoles tickle the ribs of streamlets and loughs.

But what the soldier might give to see a rainbow
spanning the cove, or a school of basking sharks
swimming nose-to-tail just offshore,
or sunlight shimmering a waterlogged 'fulacht fiadh',
has faded with him. As for arguing the world

or its wear, or whether the heather painting the hills
is red or purple, orange or green,
we doubt such matters would cost him a thought
if he could live his life over. One house
owns a wireless, and with the 'big people' gathered

to hear far-off, bellicose, defiant voices,
we climb the forbidden graveyard wall, embed spikes
of foxglove, 'dead man's fingers', where
we tread, supposing the soldier's feet, supposing
his head. And climb again when we are older:

/ poem continues

courting couples wanting privacy, wanting to feel
our bodies eased away; find ourselves
led—after we bundle and kiss—to recollect him sunken
in the clay-covered dark, to imagine a love
of his own and how maybe she waits, still waits,

the war ten years ended. Ten years, ten more,
the grist of decades anchors and layers us. The wall
stands, and beyond it other walls, each
a front for something—peace, prayer, commemoration,
even the notion that the dead, if permitted

to mingle, might twist, as the living do, old grievance
into fresh feud. He lingers, almost a fiction,
yet niggling us until we must clear the 'buttermilk' moss
that smothers his bed. Hold a ceremony,
someone says, find and invite his relatives, but first

knock down the dividing wall. Our shoes bruise
the damp, hillside grass. Politicians and military men extol
the soldier's sacrifice. An orphan, we hear, born
in Wales; kind, helpful, quick with a joke.
And—the speaker smiles, clears his throat—a Catholic.

Patrick Deeley

Parlance

Anne Hayden

We arrive at the door wearing crumpled shirts and armed with paper cups of take-away coffee. There used to be a free coffee machine here but that went out with the cutbacks, as did the plants at reception and claiming expenses for taxis home. Since the Charlie Hebdo attacks, we no longer complain about the security guards and swipe card system complicating our journey to the newsroom. Nous sommes Charlie, we like to think, although sub-editors and satirists are hardly the same thing. None of us comments on the fact that some of us carry the paper cups with shaky hands. Stephen Lynch, who was off yesterday, sits down at his desk, then gets back up, his face red. 'This isn't my chair,' he says, 'who's after swapping my chair?' Stephen's chair is one of the ergonomically designed ones that the company no longer has the budget to buy and is therefore highly covetable. As he marches through the open-plan office, lifting jackets from the backs of chairs to check for the Tippex marking he had put on his, the rest of us type in our passwords and wait for the machines to boot up. 'Fifty-three years old and having a hissy fit about a chair,' Brian Murphy says, as if it's something unusual, which it's not.

We log into our screens when most people are getting to the end of their day's work, and we log out when they're already tucked up in bed. Under the fluorescent lighting, we recap the statistics from the night before. 4am, no 5am, the last person left the lock-in, nobody can be certain. A sensible four pints, an honest eight pints, could have been twelve pints for the 5am stragglers. Our drinking rate is high, our divorce rate's through the roof. Stories start to fill up our inboxes, looking to be reshaped, untangled, cleaned up and cut back, in need of headlines, subheads and captions. We rewrite them using words we never use in common parlance: lag for inmate, tot for baby, boffin for scientist, probe for investigation. We replace man with lad because that big fat m takes up too much headline space, the nice slender l is so much less unwieldy. We create our own abbreviations: prez for president, ambo for ambulance. We put an asterisk in the word tit next to a picture of a pair of barely covered t*ts. Was it for this we got our Masters degrees? There's a squeal of horror from behind Myra Duggan's screen. 'That's disgusting,' she says, 'sickos!' We gather around her desk to see the photo of a tortured dog attached to an ISPCA story she is subbing. Myra, one of the few women among us, zooms in on the image of the red setter, scrawny and with red welts where a glossy coat should be, something oozing out of his eye. We wince and recoil and say things like 'Animals!' and 'That's a disgrace!' and 'The poor pup.'

Stephen Lynch comes back from the other end of the newsroom followed by a girl we don't recognise, an intern on the features desk we later learn, who wheels his chair ahead of her and looks close to tears. It's almost a rite of passage, when a new person starts, to be at the end of a Stephen Lynch tirade, but then new people don't start here anymore. The revolving door only lets people out now, not in. When Stephen goes out for his first cigarette of the day, Joe McCormack says 'It's only a matter of time before that guy goes postal.' 'He could go all Michael Douglas in *Falling Down* any day now,' Finbarr O'Leary, the chief sub, says. We laugh, maybe a little too loudly. Everyone knows Stephen has a rifle collection on display at home; we don't know how we know this as none of us has been in his house, but we know it all the same. Rifles and cocaine habits are rarely a good combination. It's another slow news day, silly season seems to have spilled from August into September. We're bored and entertain ourselves by seeing how far we can push things. A headline on a picture of Gisele Bundchen modelling underwear—Gis in her pants—gets vetoed but one about a GAA player taking his fiancée up the aisle slips through. Some of us secretly work on our novels or screenplays as we wait for the reporters to file copy, others write short stories set, for example, in the newsroom of a tabloid newspaper during the dying days of print journalism.

A phone rings. There's a flurry of activity from the news desk, a bank of computers facing each other, five a side, mirroring our own desk. A school bus has crashed bringing a group of teenage girls home from their convent secondary. The editor strides out of his office. 'Any dead?' 'We don't know yet.' 'We'll splash it if there are.' Finally, something has happened. A reporter and a photographer are dispatched to the scene, another reporter sent to the school. If anyone is dead, they'll call to the family's front door looking for a line, any line, even if it's just 'the family were too distraught to comment'. We stay at our desks and carry on with our work. We don't dirty our hands with doorstepping and death knocks, wouldn't know how to hack a phone. We simply edit the stories that come from the death knocks, which is not the same thing at all. On the bus to work, we might have read the *Guardian*, or maybe some Dostoyevsky, but we leave our liberal views and literary notions at the office door. Crime and punishment is one of our big themes but our subject matter is reality TV, gangland murders and love-rat footballers. We brand anyone who has ever kicked a ball a 'footie ace', while a woman in a bikini on a beach is always 'showing her ex what he's missing'. Ill people are 'brave' and dead people are almost always 'tragic'. Drug use must be associated with shame or remorse, 'my cocaine hell'. Extra-marital affairs are the ultimate crime. Alliteration is good, as in 'pint-sized popstar Ronan Keating', rhyming is better, as in 'pop flop', puns are the best, see 'How do you solve a problem like Korea?' We don't pun on death but we joke about it a lot. Sure if you don't laugh, you'll… well, it's not that we'd cry, we're men, most of us, but you have to laugh. How else would we get a paper out night after night?

Stephen Lynch bashes his phone receiver onto the desk three times, he has been trying to get in touch with a reporter who has spelt a murder accused's surname two different ways but the reporter is not answering his phone. An email comes through from HR, subject line: Attention all staff. There's a collective intake of breath before we click on the link. The last round of redundancies was almost six months ago, the axe is sure to fall again soon. And when Mark Daly left last month to start an entry-level public relations job—jumping from the sinking ship as he said—he wasn't replaced. Mark Daly leaving was an anomaly. While the rest of us might complain about the increasing workload and lowering standards, none of us leaves by choice, where would we go? Our skills are no longer transferable; it's no coincidence that the word thesaurus sounds like a type of dinosaur. The email is about the HR manager's yogurts going missing from the fridge. 'We seem to have dodged the bullet for another day,' Stephen Lynch says, his choice of terminology further confirming our suspicions that he's a gun nut. But there's always the possibility of a P45. Fact-checking is no longer valued in our post-Trump post-truth society. No one cares about syntax or apostrophes anymore and clever headlines don't work as well online. We live in fear of the march of the worldwide web, terrorised by terms such as click bait and data analytics. Stephen Lynch's friend at a newspaper across town told him they've got rid of their sub-editors altogether and have reporters filing copy directly on to the page. Reporters who don't know the difference between lose and loose, who don't know when to use it's or its, who end sentences with prepositions. We're an endangered species, at risk of extinction, waiting for the wheels to come off the bus. It doesn't bother Joe McCormack who is just serving out his time until a pay-off allows him move to the south of France and write that novel he's always going on about… or about which he's always going on… sometimes it's difficult not to finish on a preposition. Joe likes to tell us about the days of editing by hand, literally cutting out words with a knife, the days of four-day weeks and four pints at lunchtime, smoking at the desk and a bottle of whiskey in the drawer. Don't get him started on how there was no such thing as Google. He is paid twice as much as the rest of us for half the work, although he claims his three ex-wives have left him flat broke. He'll be in for a nice package when he gets out of here—as long as he doesn't go the way of the old chief sub who never missed a day's work in forty-five years, then dropped dead a week after retirement.

Several people have gathered around Brian Murphy's desk and are watching something on his screen. Their sounds and comments suggest it's a football video—wait for it… this is it… ooooh… straight through… I can't look… show us the replay. But when we join the growing cluster around Brian's workstation, we see it's a video of a man being beheaded by ISIS terrorists, it comes clean off and rolls across the yellow sandstone of what looks like a town square, the decapitated kneeling body stays upright for another few seconds. The Yogurtgate email is followed by one from a sports reporter looking for sponsorship for running the Dublin marathon next month. He took up running last year after a heart scare made him swap chips for chip times and now he talks about nothing else. We kept a roster of visitors alongside our work rosters while he was in the hospital, we're at our best in a crisis. Joe McCormack is the first to donate to his refugees fundraising page, he puts himself down for twenty euro, making it impossible for the rest of us to give less without looking tight. Easy for him, we think, with his mortgage paid off and no childcare costs. It's for a good cause, we know, but surely a tenner would have been fine.

A phone rings. A young girl has died in the bus crash. Tragic teen we'll call her and use her first name, innocent victims get first names. Fifteen years old. Pretty. We know she's pretty because someone has already trawled her Facebook profile for photos. And it's always so much more tragic when they're pretty. If Lisa Dwyer was here she'd point out that we wouldn't use an equivalent adjective if it was a boy who had died, we wouldn't call him a tragic hunk, but Lisa's off today. There are occasionally small victories for feminism, vetoing the use of the word funbags for breasts, for example, by arguing that they're not fun for everyone, or quietly changing Miriam O'Callaghan's description from 'yummy mummy' to 'Prime Time presenter'—not that Miriam would probably care. But these small battles will not win the war. Last week Lisa changed Amal

Clooney's description from George Clooney's wife to human rights lawyer but when she returned to the page later she found it had been revised to human rights hottie. The page plans on our screens start to fill up like a giant puzzle. A full page is devoted to another paedophile on trial. Evil paedo. Sick perv. Vile sex beast. Monster. Paedo priest works well for alliteration. We'll keep the details out though, people don't want to read about anal rape while they're eating their cornflakes. There's an unwritten, unspoken rule that Finbarr O'Leary never has to sub one of those stories, the same way it's understood that Lisa Dwyer doesn't do baby stories after her stillborn last year.

A hospital in Syria has been bombed, forty-seven dead, including eleven children. Three paragraphs in a corner of page 16. A right-hand page is given over to a soap 'star' who has been caught cheating on his catalogue-model partner—a bit of showbiz to lighten things up. Sex sells but we never call it plain old sex, it's romping, nooky, between-the-sheets action. Soon she'll be on *I'm a Celebrity… Get Me Out of Here* eating live insects in the jungle, wearing a bikini, showing him what he's missing. A boat carrying 200-plus migrants has sunk in the Aegean Sea, thirty-seven still missing, presumed dead. It's the third one this week so will hardly make it in unless the photos are any good. Madonna has had a nip slip on stage at an awards show, that will definitely make it in. Some nut thinks he's seen Madeleine McCann in Venezuela, might make a page lead. A man has jumped forty feet into the canal basin from a ledge near Boland's Mill as some sort of 'performance art' stunt. The copy for this story has been swiped from an art website. It reads: 'Acclaimed painter James Maguire has transcended his chosen medium and made a daring statement about the impermanence of art and the superficial nature of the art world. Maguire, whose abstract expressionist painting on a wall near Boland's Mill caused a stir both on and offline yesterday, painted over the work early today with a caricature of himself and the word "fraud" before jumping from a forty-foot ledge into the canal basin below.' They wait until seventy words in to tell us the good part? There's another 567 words of this to be boiled down into three short paragraphs but our readers don't care much for abstract expressionism. Something like this will do:

> A GRAFFITI artist has cheated death after plunging 40ft into a canal basin in a brazen publicity stunt.
> Potty painter James Maguire, 27, carried out the wacky dive at Boland's Mill in Dublin yesterday.
> An onlooker said: 'Watching it was terrifying, it would nearly give you an art attack.'

Onlookers are good like that, they always have the perfect quote for the story, great for the puns. We bounce around a few headline ideas, it's a short space to allow room for the picture: Graf lad's daft leap—too long, doesn't fit. Graf gaffe—too short. Pick-up artist—just not good enough. Nice spray for a swim—won't fit even with squeezing the font size down way beyond the rules. 'What a head the ball anyway,' Stephen Lynch says. 'Total chancer,' Joe McCormack adds. 'Off the wall,' Brian Murphy says. Off the wall—that'll do, it fits. We eat our take-away dinners from plastic containers at our desks. Myra Duggan complains about the smell of chips while she eats her Marks & Spencer's superfood salad. In between consuming fast food and subbing stories, we discuss the latest Scandi-noir detective series and bet on the horses. We know a bit about everything and can talk about anything—World War Two history or teutonic thrash metal—as long as it doesn't involve our personal lives. 'There's a nice sunset out there,' Myra says, even though the blinds on the windows are down. 'Lots of people are posting pictures of it on Twitter.'

Brian Murphy jumps out of his seat and shouts 'Yes!', spilling chips all over his keyboard and knocking over the pile of old newspapers cluttering his desk. We look up at the TV screens that surround us, Messi has gone 3-1 up for Barcelona. 'That's it, good man!' Brian says. Myra Duggan rolls her eyes and tells Brian to take it easy, that Messi can't hear him. Everyone knows Brian and Myra are sleeping together. They haven't told us, in fact they pretend not to like each other and never leave the office together, but we know. We can't remember how we know, but we know—even if Myra's husband doesn't. We always know. As deadline approaches, we sit forward more, hunch closer to our screens, type faster on our keyboards, manspread less. We x out of the book writing and the betting browsers. The reporters have gone home and the phones have stopped ringing, the clickety click-click of the keyboards is punctuated only by the odd expletive. By 10.30pm, it's almost all in the bag with half an hour to go, a rare early finish is on the cards, creamy pints are within reach.

A phone rings. There's been a shooting in west Dublin, a gangland thing. The victim is critical in hospital, fighting for his life as we say. 'Could they not have the decency to shoot each other earlier in the day?' Finbarr O'Leary says; it's a tired old joke. The victim is low down the scale, probably not worth a splash. There's a hierarchy: crime lords and drugs bosses at the top, gangsters and mobsters below, henchmen, hoods and thugs at the bottom. We'll refer to him by his surname, criminals don't get honorifics and only the big guns get nicknames: The Monk, The Penguin, The Dapper Don. They have to earn those badges of honour. We breathe a sigh of relief when we're told we're sticking with the pretty dead girl for page one. We finish our jobs, put the paper to bed, read and reread the front page. Girl, 15, dies in horror school bus smash. No need for clever wordplay in a situation like this. Tributes from her Facebook page fill out the copy. 'U were taken too soon, I never thought I'd loose you, rip my angel xxx.' They've gone big on the photo of the teenager, looks like a selfie taken on a night out, she's wearing a bodycon dress and too much eyeliner and looks older than her fifteen years. Above the story are Messi's hat-trick and Madonna's nipple, and another blurb flagging up the horoscopes special. 'That's it, we're all in.' We don't wait to be told twice, start to put on our coats.

Then the phone rings again. Joe McCormack answers it, and shouts 'What do you mean she's not dead?' A pause, then 'Shit.' We're already taking our coats back off when he hangs up and announces, 'That was the stringer, she's on life support still.' Finbarr O'Leary says, 'For fuck's sake. Call the senders and tell them to hold the front page. We'll splash the shooting instead. Move it up to page 5 inside, move the bus crash back.' We turn our computers back on. Joe grumbles about a missed bus (fine for you, we think, you can afford the taxi) and Stephen Lynch mutters under his breath about last orders. Myra Duggan says, 'Well, that's good, that she survived, that girl, only fifteen years old, imagine,' and we agree, chastened. And Brian Murphy says, 'Good thing we caught it, heads would roll tomorrow if we killed off a teenager.' We agree again, more vocally this time. We get the job done quickly, we could do these gangland shooting stories in our sleep. We play it up a bit, push him further up the ranks for the front page in 90-point upper-case bold. Blasted in broad daylight: Gang boss fights for life after shooting. The kids will look up to him now. Broad daylight is a slight exaggeration too but there is still a stretch in the evenings. 'I need a pint after all that,' Finbarr O'Leary says. He won't be short of company. The alternative is sitting up alone binge-watching Netflix or lying awake in the dark as our partners sleep—those of us who still have partners that is—as we wait for the adrenaline to wear off. So we drink and we smoke and we drink some more. Because how else would we sleep at night?

Starving With Bobby Sands

Bobby Sands was starving himself, Mum told us.
Somewhere in Ireland, in prison.
Putting my peanut butter on white sandwich into a plastic bag,

Mum started raving on
about someone called Gandhi then,
and people who died for something.

It was mass day and when the bells rang out at eleven,
I thought of Bobby Sands
and wondered what he'd done.

By noon I was hungry. Eating my lunch
at my desk I watched Sister Gemma sink her small teeth
into a bun thick with spread.

Each day Mum read the papers, watched the news,
and reported. Bobby Sands was still starving.
Why he was starving I never really knew.

Something about England, Ireland, freedom,
her majesty's prison, a parliament, religion,
the IRA, and Catholics who didn't like Protestants.

At our house Mum liked everyone. We all went off
to mass each Sunday. Sometimes Mum went too.
Other times she took herself to hear Baptists sing,

Evangelicals preach, Lutherans pray.
Sometimes she went to the library.
For several weeks Bobby didn't eat

and we went on watching him,
Mum raving to us about independence,
courage, what it meant to hunger for something.

Out of sympathy, we started fasting once a week.
Friday was Hunger Strike lunch.
Instead of a peanut butter sandwich and cookies,

I ate nothing. At noon I excused myself
to the girls' room. Nosy Mary Ellen followed,
asking where was my food.

We're starving with Bobby Sands, I told her.
She rolled her eyes. I wished my mother were the kind
who shopped or bowled. Instead she read and wept.

Soon everyone was asking who was Bobby Sands
and why was he starving. By day's end
I had been called to the principal's office

where I reported that at home things were just fine,
but that somewhere in England or Ireland,
Bobby Sands was starving to death in prison.

Tess Barry

A Ghazal of Exodus

Cradled in a rush ark, in the leaf-green Nile, Moses
floats downstream, where parted reeds disclose him near to home.

    *

A Chalayan* coffee-table can be donned and worn—
saving time when on short notice to leave home.

    *

In nineteen-forty-seven, *SS Exodus* sets
sail for Palestine, the closest it can get to home.

    *

Leaving Babylon behind, the Rastafarians
turn their eyes to Ethiopia, their Zion home.

    *

Shark-shoals follow coffin-ships, feeding on the bodies
of the dead, thrown overboard en route from home.

    *

Bibles open at *Exodus*, St Kildans
bid farewell to their remote Atlantic island home.

    *

Millions of the displaced become convinced
that an over-laden boat is safer than their home.

    *

Silence in Calais jungle, where stitched-up lips protest
at bull-dozed shanties—the make-shift substitute for home.

    *

Do we not hear alarm bells when this Earth's people surge
across the globe, flowing like the rain away from home?

Amanda Bell

*Hussein Chalayan is the maker of a set of portable furniture, inspired by the
designer's thinking on the wartime impermanence that finds homes raided
and families forced to flee or be killed.

Hunter-gatherers

Louise Kennedy

The hare wasn't ten feet away, the closest he had ever come. He was bigger than Siobhan had realised, legs stocky, white tail cartoon-fluffy. In spite of his heft there was a lightness in the way he flumped about. He paused, held himself very straight. Siobhan fancied he was looking at her, though it was unlikely he could see her. The back garden was shaded by a dense grove of sally trees and the winter light was thin.

'He's there again now. You told me they only come out at night.'

'You'll often see them at this time, or in the evening,' said Sid. He leaned into her back, pushing her against the sink, and banged the kitchen window with the heel of his hand. In a single leap the hare cleared the beech saplings Sid had planted in the autumn, ears making a V sign, and took off in the direction of the House.

'You frightened him.'

'Cheeky bastard's after tipping my new hedge.'

'He's beautiful.'

'He? It, you mean. The thing's a pest, Townie.' He lifted her hair and rubbed his chin across the nape of her neck.

'Stop.'

'You know you want to.'

'You're not funny.'

The Pajero puttered to a halt outside. 'I'm gone,' she said and made for the bedroom. Sid caught her wrist.

'Say hello at least, don't be ignorant.'

Siobhan pulled her fleece across herself, wishing she had put a bra on. Paddy let himself in and stood on the hearth rug in his boots. He and Sid wore identical camouflage hunting jackets in shades of russet and olive and brown. It was the last day of the shooting season. Siobhan and Sid rented the gate lodge of the country estate owned by the Fitzroy family that was known for its wild game and salmon. Paddy was the gamekeeper, Sid one of the beaters. They had been friends since school.

'Well,' Paddy said. In one hand he had a bottle of poitín that he gave to Sid. Two small dead birds dangled from the other. He offered them to Siobhan with a sidelong look at Sid. Both men laughed when she shrank back. Paddy followed Sid to the kitchen. He had parked so close to the porch diesel fumes were panting into the sitting room. Siobhan went to close the front door. Dogs were yelping from the back of the jeep, and a slight girl was in the passenger seat, limp dark hair framing a small face. She was wearing a waxed jacket that was too big for her and a man's tweed cap. Siobhan gestured at her to come in. The girl raised an eyebrow and a shoulder and looked the other way. Siobhan left the door ajar and went into the kitchen.

'Who's the young one?' she asked Paddy.

'Rachael. The girlfriend's daughter.'

'Should she not be in school?'

'She's in Transition Year. She was at me to bring her dog with her to train it.'

'Bring her in, sure.'

'She's grand where she is.'

'I'll be late this evening,' said Sid. He kissed her forehead. 'Champagne and canapés with Lady Muck, and a few scoops in Dolan's.'

'Well for you,' Siobhan said, backing towards the bedroom. The previous morning Paddy had kissed her goodbye too. And sniffed her. *Like a dog*, she had told Sid. Sid had just laughed.

'Paddy's a hunter. A man's man.'

'He's a creep, Sid.'

She stood on the porch and watched them leave. Rachael answered her wave with a stare. Paddy reversed onto the lawn and took off towards the House; on his spare wheel cover there was a faded silhouette of two rhinos, one mounting the other from behind. For a second the lake glinted beyond them, a silver line in the distance. She and Sid had come to live here the previous Easter, yet she was still moved by the place, by the pastoral sweep of parkland that stretched to the right of the cottage, how it changed every day. This morning the copse of oaks before the bend was crisp with hoarfrost.

She ladled water from the rain barrel at the side of the house and sloshed it around the cyclamen she had potted on either side of the door, taking care not to let the icy water touch the leaves. She thought the lodge beautiful. It was a scaled down model of the House, generous in width yet only one room deep, with four small Grecian columns holding up a miniature portico. Vanessa Fitzroy had had it painted in Farrow & Ball colours and hung Liberty print curtains. Now it was winter, though, white mould bloomed on the walls and several times a day Siobhan blotted condensation from the windows with an old towel.

She went back inside and through to the kitchen. The dead birds were on the draining board. She flipped one of them over with a wooden spoon, saw a flash of jade at the wing tip, the fine, tiny nib of its beak. It was a teal. She put the kettle on for a cup of tea. Sid said they should buy local produce, and was keen for her to drink a herbal infusion made by an English woman who was living off the grid near Drumshanbo. Siobhan thought it smelled like silage, that Barry's of Cork was local enough.

Sid had bought books online about self-sufficiency and foraging. For the month of February they would eat only wild food. It would be a lean month for plants and leaves, he said, but they would manage. The freezer was full of nettle puree and wild garlic pesto. At the summer's end they had gathered stuff she hadn't known was food and preserved it. On the kitchen dresser there were jars of pickled alexanders and rowan jelly, bottles of sloe gin. There were powdered puffballs that Sid wanted her to use instead of stock cubes, pots of magic mushrooms suspended in honey. She didn't completely trust Sid with the mushrooms. Once he had brought home a deadly amanita that was full of small white worms. Later they had pegged chanterelles and hedgehog fungi to flimsy makeshift clotheslines that criss-crossed the spare bedroom. The first batch had rotted in the damp. The next was a success because they had put an electric heater on in the room for a week.

Siobhan put on a green tweed coat and mauve mohair scarf, and fur-lined ankle boots. Her mad ould one outfit, Sid called it. She drove the three miles into town and parked at the back of SuperValu. Christmas lights, disconnected and dribbling rust, were still swinging over Main Street as she crossed it. The library was housed in a former Protestant church that sat back from the street. The children's books were just inside the door on the left. A group of small girls were in a ring on the floor with their teacher, weaving Brigid's crosses from rushes to mark the start of spring. The cross was said to guard a home from evil, fire and hunger. Siobhan might pick rushes at the lakeshore later, see if she remembered how to make one. Maybe it would guard them against visits from

Paddy. She returned her books and asked the assistant where she could find information about hares.

'Fifth from the left, third shelf down,' said a high, quick voice behind her. She turned to see who had spoken. It was Oliver Doody. He was sitting in the study area, two large rectangular tables pushed together. Opposite him, two schoolgirls were giggling over the 'Out and About' pages of the *Sligo Champion*. To their right a young black man was filling in a form.

Soon she found what she wanted. All the chairs were taken except the one next to Oliver Doody. She sat down. Oliver had been in Sid's class in school. Siobhan had often seen him walking the roads far from his bungalow on the edge of the town. His lawn swayed knee-high, and children threw stones at his windows. Today he was wearing a wide sou'wester and shiny golf jacket. One leg of his tracksuit bottoms was torn from inside the thigh to below the knee. His leg was pale and shapely. Four thick biographies of Elizabeth 1st were stacked in front of him. Siobhan opened an old *Encyclopaedia of Wildlife* and found the right chapter. It had photographs of mountain hares, European hares, American jackrabbits.

Oliver Doody cleared his throat. Siobhan turned to look at him. 'Lepus timidus hibernicus,' he said, eyes bright behind the greasy lenses of his glasses, the Latin words grave and glottal, like a spell. He told her that the Irish hare doesn't turn white in winter. He told her the Druids thought the hare was an incarnation of the moon goddess Eostre, who we named Easter after. He told her that Boudica once released a hare from under her skirt before a battle, and that the hare was on the old Irish threepenny bit. He told her it had been thought that the young males boxed out of rivalry, but that scientists now know the females box the males away when they don't want to copulate. He told her the ancient Irish believed hares were shape shifters, related to the sidhe, because a hare screams like a woman when it's hurt. Around the table, the girls had stopped giggling, the young man had put down his pen.

'A hare comes into my garden,' Siobhan said. 'I can't wait to see it leaping round the place in March.' But the spell was broken and Oliver Doody was quiet. He folded back into himself and picked at a long thread on the open seam of his bottoms. As she went to put back the books, he reached forward and tapped one of them with yellowy fingers. She borrowed it at the desk on the way out.

She went into SuperValu. Her shopping list was short, just milk, eggs and bananas. On her way to pay, a woman stopped her.

'Well, stranger.' Nicola Leyden was smiling, baring teeth so white they seemed to luminesce. She was wearing a black and pink kimono with her name on it. Her beauty clinic was above the supermarket. 'What are you up to?'

'I was in the library.'

'Weirdo. Do me a favour, will you?' She took ten euro from her pocket. 'Would you ever buy me a box of super plus and a bag of towels?'

'Do you not want to get the discount on them?'

'Davy Feeney is over the checkouts today. I'd die if he knew.'

'You have a kid to him. He must know you have periods.'

'His wife let herself go. I want to keep the bit of glamour going.'

As Siobhan approached the checkouts, Davy Feeney disappeared through a door marked PRIVATE. The doughy boy behind the counter looked miserably at the contents of her basket and had to scan the tampons three times before the till recognised the code. Siobhan wondered if Sid would like her to spend her periods squatting in a hedgerow with a wad of dock leaves, like Queen Maeve. She sniggered, out loud. The boy fled, knocking against a display of Valentine's Day cards. Nicola was waiting at the back of the shop.

'How's life with Bear Grylls?' she said, tucking her supplies under her arm.

'Grand. Last day of the shooting season today.'

'You're like death.'

'Thanks.'

'Come up to me later and I'll do your tan.'

'You'd want to be lightening yours. You're the colour of a brick.'

'I couldn't give two shites. Fake is fake. Have you time for a cup of coffee?'

Siobhan wanted to go home and read the library book before Sid came back. She made an excuse. They hugged and said they would see each other soon.

Oliver Doody was by the bottle bins, flicking curry chips into his mouth with his fingers, hunched and feral again away from the library. She paused to say hello but he didn't lift his head. Sid said Oliver Doody had been persecuted at school. Siobhan wondered if Sid had been one of his tormentors. Before the Garda station closed, Sid's father had been the Sergeant. Sid, the copper's kid. Considering he knew everything that went on in the town, Sergeant Hennigan had been oblivious to his son's drug peddling, to his fighting and thieving. Still, surely Sid would have hunted more artful prey than Oliver?

On the way home she called in to Great Gas for diesel. She bought a chicken fillet roll and a diet Coke too. In three days she would be living off the land and the prospect depressed her. When she pulled up at the lodge, she could hear shots in the distance. Sid had been home. He had left a change of clothes across the back of the couch. She brought them out to the car and drove towards the House; otherwise Paddy would drive him home to get them, and Sid would ask him in again.

It was only three but already the sky had dimmed. To the left of the house the dark lake lapped against the reeds and rushes. The gunfire was getting louder as she turned right towards the coach yard. Jeeps and trailers and small white vans were parked along the lane, the Pajero at the end. She left her car around the corner and followed the shouts and shots and barks.

They were in an open space in the field that bordered the hazel wood. Ten men were standing at posts positioned at regular intervals in a row. Paddy and Sid and the other beaters were beyond the coach yard. Suddenly pheasants flew up, a little flock of ten or twelve. They seemed to Siobhan to be disorientated, flapping weakly. There was a shout and the men at the posts had time to raise their guns and fire. Six birds fell and the dogs ran to retrieve them. A seventh bird, which Siobhan had seen take a hit, flew on towards the lake, sinking into the horizon as it struggled. She waited for one of the beaters to send a dog after it, but they just stood there. She started to walk towards Sid. She hadn't thought to put her wellingtons on and the heavy ground sucked at her heels.

'One of the birds is wounded. You need to bring a dog over to the lake,' she told Sid. Paddy whispered something to Rachael that made her smirk.

'They can fly half a mile like that. We'd never find it,' said Sid, without looking at her. She pushed his clothes at him and went back to the car, her righteous gait hampered by the wrong footwear. On the way down the lane she had to brake hard to avoid hitting a stick legged bird with no plumage, just tufts of thin white down. Vanessa Fitzroy was behind it, swathed in cashmere the colour of heather, swinging a blackthorn shillelagh. Siobhan wound the window down.

'What the fuck is that?' she said.

'Henrietta is a rescue hen, poor thing.'

'They're slaughtering healthy birds up there. Why would you rescue that yoke?'

Bridie, the cleaning lady, had told Siobhan that Vanessa spent her days lying on the couch eating chicken nuggets and Face-timing her friends in Cape Town. Vanessa had invited Siobhan to the house for coffee a few times, but by the look on her face now, she was unlikely to ask her again. Siobhan closed her window and drove too fast towards the cottage, wanting to get away from the House, too angry to stop by the lake for reeds.

Inside, she lit a fire. The twigs and shoots Sid gathered were always damp so the room grew smoky. At the sink she washed the breakfast dishes, trying not to look at the little dead birds, or think about the wounded pheasant flitting away from the men's guns. Sid's copy of Richard Mabey's *Food for Free* was propped open on the window sill. He had bought it a few months earlier and already it had begun to yellow and curl. It occurred to Siobhan he had aged it on purpose. She made another cup of tea and brought it to the sitting room. The fire had caught and was spitting brightly. She took out the book Oliver Doody had recommended. It was an anthology of folk tales collected by Yeats, with faded art nouveau illustrations. She began to read a story called 'Bewitched Butter', about a magical cow in Donegal.

Sid came home after seven, with Paddy and Rachael. He hadn't changed his clothes.

'Drink!' he said. Siobhan went to the kitchen after him.

'What's the story?'

'Relax. They're only here for one or two.'

'What age is that girl?'

'Fuck knows. Will you have one?' He waved the poitin at her. 'Lighten up, will you?' he said when she didn't answer. He brought the bottle to the sitting room with three shot glasses. Rachael was on the couch beside Paddy, flushed. Siobhan forced a smile.

'How did you get on today, Rachael?'

'It was cool.'

'I was thinking about that poor pheasant,' Siobhan said. Sid glanced at Paddy.

'There was a rake of them hit like that,' Rachael said, raising the eyebrow and shoulder again.

'That ould Yank only half hit most of his, the fucking eejit,' said Sid. 'All the right gear and he couldn't kill shite.' The others laughed.

Siobhan took her book and went down the hall. Sid would tell her later it was all her own fault, that she wasn't on the same buzz as them. She lay on top of the bed and tried to ignore Sid flicking through tracks on his iPod, Paddy's voice, slow and careful, Rachael's sudden laughter. Siobhan knew Sid would settle on 'Kashmir'. Still, when she heard the opening bars she felt a lurch of something, of fury almost, that surprised her. She would avoid him for the rest of the evening, have a long bath when the others left. The volume went up a couple of notches, bass thudding in the walls. If she asked them to turn it down there would be a row, so she stayed in the bedroom, the book in her lap unopened, and waited.

Outside in the garden the sensor light came on. The music stopped, truncating a guitar's long *waang*, there was a clattering of feet and furniture. A car door slammed, barking dogs were hushed, feet crossed the oak boards again. For a few seconds all was quiet, then from beyond the bedroom window a whisper; Sid's voice, thick with drink.

'Go *on*.'

A brisk click, then Paddy said: 'Now.'

A single shot sounded, followed by a woman's scream, long, dreadful, full of anguish. At first Siobhan just sat on the edge of the bed, her mind skittering. She went to the window, wiped her sleeve across the condensation, but could see nothing. Another shot, and this time the cry was a thin shriek that faded to a fearful gurgle. What had they done? Siobhan left the bedroom and went along the hall. The sitting room was empty, a draught coming from the open back door. Outside a wisp of gun smoke curled in the damp night and near the beech hedging a patch of grass was stained dark. The sensor light went off and, for a moment, Siobhan couldn't see. She heard a whisper, a gasp, a tiny giggle. Paddy and Rachael were beyond the kitchen windowsill. Paddy's right hand was flat on the wall, his other on the handle of the gun he was twirling into the ground, the girl looking up at him through a straggle of hair.

Siobhan went back inside. The house reeked of shit and iron and offal. She sidestepped the dark blobs on the floor and followed them to the kitchen. Sid turned from the sink and stood back. The hare was laid across the draining board, ears flopping backwards, once-white belly muddied and matted. He seemed huge, hind legs reaching beyond the kettle. There was a treacly hole at the front of his head, his eyes were hazel and still. Sid took a hunting knife from his pocket and drew it across the animal's throat, turning him quickly to catch the blood in a mug in the sink. Siobhan stumbled out the front door and steadied herself against one of the pillars. He followed her, the knife still in his hand.

'You killed him.'

'Her. It was a female. I told you this morning we'd have to get rid of it.'

'Jesus Christ. You shot her and brought her into the kitchen?'

'Rachael shot it.'

'Rachael?'

'Hit it first time. Clean. Never saw anything like it for a young one.'

'She has drink on her and you gave her a gun. She's a child.'

'Paddy said it was okay.'

'Are you mental? What is even going on with Paddy and that girl? Is he planning on driving her home?'

'He's had fuck all to drink.'

'Get them out of here or I will.'

'Fuck's sake.'

'Fine.' Siobhan went out the back. Paddy and Rachael stepped from the shadows as the light came on.

'I'm sure your mother will be wondering where you are, Rachael,' she said. Paddy nodded at the girl and she went to the jeep without a word. Sid stood on the doorstep, smiling, furious, Paddy beside him.

She went to the bedroom and closed the door. She thought of the hare, how it had taken nine or ten visits for her to come as close as she had that morning, how she had come back that evening. She pictured her near the kitchen window, pert yet timorous, hazel eyes widening in the sudden electric light. She picked up the book. It opened on the first page of a story that Yeats had written. She could hardly believe the illustration, the close thicket of trees, the candy floss tail and meaty hind legs clearing a hedge, ears in a V sign. She read the story three times. It was about a man who is led astray by a mysterious hare and is never seen again.

Sid opened the door and stood slack shouldered at the foot of the bed, in a stance of remorse.

'Look, I cleared it all up.'

'I don't want to talk to you.'

'Things die.'

'She didn't just die.'

'We're in the countryside. I thought you got it.'

'I thought you weren't a prick.' The book was still open in her lap.

Sid knelt on the floor beside Siobhan. He put a strand of her hair behind her ear and dragged a thumb across her cheek. His hand smelled like slaughter.

Ríocht an Chait

Crónán ar chaoinchois
breacbhuí sa gharraí oíche
réaltaí ag spréachadh
buí órga i logaill a chinn.

Meán oíche shleamhain,
é ag fiafraí cúis mo sheasta
sa ghairdín fhuar ag séideadh
toit sa bhealach air.

Comhairlíonn sé mo thiontú
faghairt ina shúile glé
is strainséar ina chríocha mé
cúlaím is fágaim a ríocht.

Amárach, beidh an ghrian ina suí
is tabharfaidh mé a dhúshlán.
Anocht, tarraingím blaincéad
fá mo cheann chun a chuid gártha

a chur ar neamhní.

Proinsias Mac a' Bhaird

Cat's Kingdom

He purrs on padded feet,
stippled amber in the night
as stars spark gold
from his eyes.

Slick as midnight, he's asking
what has me in his cold garden
blowing smoke
across his path.

His advice: *get lost*,
his eyes glint a warning—
I'm the stranger here,
so I retreat beyond his borders.

Tomorrow with the sun in situ,
I'll throw down a gauntlet,
for now I'll shroud my head
in blankets, stifle the smart

of his jeers.

Jessica Traynor a d'aistrigh

Father Bradley

Father Bradley, go ndéana Dia a mhaith air,
léadh sé Aifreann gasta i gcónaí
is ligeadh sé dúinn na ceisteanna a chur,
níor ceileadh a dhath faoi éadaí eaglasta.

Dá mbeimis le hiomann úr a cheol,
ní chun Dia a adhradh ach chun é a cheistiú
chun é a dhíthógáil is a scrúdú
chun é a chur ar a thriail os comhair an phobail,

déarfadh sé go dtig an fuath
i gcuideachta an fháis,
go gcaithfear carn mór aoiligh a thógáil
sula dtig na préataí i gceart.

'When a gardener sings to the stinking mud
he cares little for melody or pitch,
his grace notes fall on filth and slime
his cadence is that of the muck.
The day may be when a bluebell
comes to sing along in time, but sometimes,'
ar sé go bog ag smaointiú,
'bluebells never chime!'

Father Bradley, go ndéana Dia a mhaith air
tá sagairt mar é ag éirí gann,
bhíodh an t-Aifreann gasta
ach mhair an tseanmóir i bhfad.

Proinsias Mac a' Bhaird

Father Bradley

Father Bradley, God be good to him,
read a speedy mass,
begged our questions,
kept no secrets in his cassock pockets.

When he had us sing hymns,
it was to harmonise our doubts,
dissect God's polyphony;
trial every note and word.

He'd say hatred and growth
were fertile bedfellows,
and the biggest dung heap
grew the best spuds.

'When a gardener sings to the stinking mud
he cares little for melody or pitch,
his grace notes fall on filth and slime
his cadence is that of the muck.
The day may be when a bluebell
comes to sing along in time, but sometimes,'
he would reflect,
'bluebells never chime!'

Father Bradley, God bless him,
his like are growing scarce—
the mass was always quick,
but the sermons lingered.

Jessica Traynor a d'aistrigh

On Gesture: A Broken Genealogy in 9 Movements

Doireann Ní Ghríofa

i. Beckon

August. Drizzle blows up from the Atlantic, over the Kerry playground where my children run. Wind draws a shriek from an empty swing. This is our summer holiday. Nearby, a girl, alone on a bench. Under her raincoat, a shudder. I am the only adult here. She wipes her nose, leaving a snail-trail of mucus on a waterproof sleeve. From a fist, my index finger juts out, hooking back twice. The gesture draws her closer. Wordlessly, it communicates: *Come to me.* But I am a stranger. She is afraid. She has been taught to avoid unknowns. Still, my gesture draws her body so close that I can whisper: [   ]

ii. Listen

Her hand cups an ear, her brow lifts, her chin tilts; from this arrangement, I understand that she cannot quite hear me. The wind has stolen my words, and lifted them away, over the waves. I lean towards her and try again. I raise my voice a notch or two and say: [Cé leis tú?]

iii. Shrug

Her shoulders lift and drop, the motion speaking for her closed mouth, where the edges of her lips turn down. Incomprehension: our country's linguistic history condensed in a single gesture. I chose a phrase that meant *Who do you belong to?* and *From which people do you come?* but now I change my tongue to the cold, firm words she knows. I begin to ask 'Where's your…?' and she smiles, her head bobs twice, but again, a shrug. I am wondering what to ask next when a car draws up. She runs towards it. Her face behind the foggy window seems different already. She waves.

Every child is a changeling. I have birthed four live infants; I have watched four grow. Like all children, they wake up each day sturdier, having absorbed and assimilated yesterday's unwieldly new skill or word. Every child is a killer; in their sleep, they slay the child of yesterday. It's easily done. Ask a child what happened to the boy he was before and he doesn't need to speak to explain. The gesture says it all. A shrug. *Oh, him? Gone. He's gone.*

iv. Wave

A rented caravan. I stand in the kitchen, watching my infant daughter wave me goodbye. She lifts an arm, fingers extended, and flicks her chubby wrist resolutely. At first I think it must be chance, an accidental fling of the fingers, some instinct or reflex, but she repeats the gesture until it becomes undeniable. Her wave is as clear as the farewell of any young woman leaving forever, a pale hanky raised and fluttering on the deck of a ship, waving over the waves to those who reciprocate from the shore, those who stand and wave back, knowing that at some point they must decide to leave the pier and return to a kitchen that will grow dark, for the first time, in her absence. Since 1700, over 10,000,000 people born in Ireland have emigrated. That's 10^7. Ten million of us, waving goodbye.

The Departures Lounge was the first place that I saw my mother cry. As a girl in the recession of the 1980s, I remember the eerie 4am feeling of August mornings behind airport barriers, waving a beloved aunt goodbye again. Again. Over the past decade, I've waved off my own generation too. Their parents haunt the supermarkets; they push fifty cent coins into my children's fists and smile, always nodding: *Skype is great for the grandkids, ah sure, skype is great.* I think of them as I fall asleep, waving their goodbyes behind a computer screen.

The wave goodbye seems tattooed inside us, but what of the baby? Was it always there, inside her, engrained in the seemingly innocuous sequence of DNA, along with all the other genetic secrets that lurk there? I wonder whether a gesture could be written into the garbled gobbledygook of a people, lettered into our genetic code. I find myself fretting over the other secrets that lurk inside her, for like every family, we have our afflictions that are handed from generation to generation. We have our own word for inherited anguish and inevitability, for the anatomy of a branch. In our family, the word is ever-present but carefully, consciously, goes unspoken. It is a single word, all angled syllables and sharp elbows. *Schizophrenia.*

v. Loop The Loop

In the schoolyard, a singsong taunt giggled its way from child to child, bringing with it a childish gesture to indicate the mad. *I curl my hair and I wipe my nose,* the circling of an index finger near the temple, the sly point. How my body remembers it, even now: the quickening pulse of repeating this gesture, of pointing away from my own head to the head of another, the deferral of shame, the passed accusation. Decoy. This gesture is a solemn inheritance that teaches a schoolgirl never to speak of a beloved family member whose entire adult life has been lived in institutions. A girl who becomes a mother whose internet search history coagulates around: [schizophrenia inheritance risk] [schizophrenia genetic probability] [symptoms schizophrenia onset].

Some studies suggest that the elevated incidence of schizophrenia in Ireland is attributable to genetic factors, while others propose that that it is a product of historical dispossession, colonial rule, the emotional destruction of a people gripped by waves of emigration, the echoing repercussions of famine.

Echokinesis is a tell-tale characteristic of schizophrenia, a mirroring in which a movement is echoed, repeated, passed on from one person to another. (*I curl my hair and I wipe my nose.*) The inheritance of schizophrenia, then, might be thought of as a manifestation of echokinesis in itself, an elaborate heirloom, a genetic convolution echoing from generation to generation, or a gesture passed hand to hand, waving goodbye, always waving goodbye, an invisible dance. Echokinesis is the diffusion of gesture from person to person, from the leaver to the left.

vi. Hunger

Either of two gestures can communicate hunger: a circular pat of a stomach or a point to an open, empty mouth. I cannot do either without the acidic tumble of gut-guilt. It is not fashionable to be angry about the historical horrors visited upon us by the English. In fact, it is decidedly unfashionable, and yet, the more I read, the more it becomes impossible to maintain any sort of shrug or glib detachment. The things they did. The things they didn't do. The things they did. The most recent period of mass starvation in Ireland was in the nineteenth century. Among the wounds inflicted by that famine was the destruction of both our language and our population. *A million dead, a million emigrated*, we learn by rote in school. The phrase rolls around a child's mouth like a glass marble, or the punchline to a grim nursery rhyme.

Count: the tonnes of food exported to England while our people starved. Count: the thousands of families evicted, their homes battered to rubble. Count: the corpses hastily buried by the roadsides where they fell. Count: the children who lay fevered in filthy workhouses, who died, and in dying, were added to the growing pile of bodies in a mass grave. Count: the 'public works' ordered to force people to labour on extending local gentry's walled demesnes, to build famine roads that led nowhere, men dying on the way. Count: the stones lifted and dropped, the drops of blood that fell from scrawled hands. Count: the 'wage'—the scoops of food or coins dropped into those torn palms. Count: the soup kitchens, count the ladles of thin sustenance, a lure to abandon culture, language, religion. Any attempt to quantify our shame will fail.

My reading draws away from scholarly works towards the small beating heart of folklore. Scanty, these sources. The generation that survived that famine and the generations who followed them were reluctant to remember, to reconstruct those dark days by speaking of them. In these records, it is referred to as 'An Drochshaol', which might be literally translated as 'The Bad Life'. The material is so unremittingly grim that the mind emigrates, and daydreams instead. Still, the subconscious clings to the most horrific images, conjuring them on the cusp of sleep: the emancipated corpse of a young woman found by a rural roadside, her mouth grass-stained. Inside her shawl, a dead baby, and clenched in his mouth, the nipple torn from the flesh of his mother's breast. Others must have limped past this starving mother and infant, turning their gaze from her outstretched hand, her plea for help. Call it survivors' guilt, call it post-traumatic stress disorder, call it what it is: a deep, lurking shame.

The colour of this shame is the green at her mouth, our national colour, the green of the land, and how it failed to provide any nourishment to her when she most needed it. The land's abundance of grain and pork and butter was busily diverted to English mouths. How she was failed. Consider her infant in his desperate suckling, failed too, and on both of their parched tongues, the syllables of a language that would soon be ruined, replaced by the tongue of those who showed such unerring efficiency in their exportation of grain and meats, of butter and linen. Their laden cartloads drove past the bodies that slowly perished on roadsides and in gutters all the way to the port. Famine-era Ireland has been described by historians as *the granary of England*, but among other significant exports during this period was tongue.

I trawl dictionaries for linguistic fossils of this history and find faint traces, a speckling in miniscule font. One phrase for 'miserly' is *tá gorta air*, which could be translated (in a very literal way) as *the famine is on him*—an acknowledgement, perhaps, that a man might carry that trauma in his body and behaviour in the decades following the hunger itself. The phrase carries the terrible heft of famine, the burden on the bones. A generation of young Irish girls sent to new lives in Australia were forced to re-live the damage wrought on their bones by the famine when they attempted to give birth. Their pelvises were so stunted by the Hunger, so brittle, so narrow, that in labour, their bones failed to let the baby's head pass through. This necessitated a horrific procedure, the craniotomy, whereby the infant's head and body had to be shattered and the dead baby birthed in pieces. Frequently, a woman survived this procedure only to become impregnated again, and be forced to repeat the procedure. This, the terrible weight of the famine on those who survived it, the burden on their bones.

The dictionary pages let us give breath to the old words, words like *gorta*. It's there in the shadows, in another little-used description: 'Ní ligfeadh an gorta dó é a dhéanamh', implying *he was too stingy to do it*, or in a more directly literal translation: *the famine wouldn't let him do it*. Do what? The famine inflicted its horrors; the famine wouldn't let him speak.

vii. Hush

A single finger pressed to lips demands obedience, demands silence.

One means of quenching the Irish language was the infliction of shame and physical punishment on children caught speaking Irish whereby they were beaten by schoolmasters until their tongues relented and turned to English. *It's for the best*, their mothers said, *you'll need English when you go*. The mothers were correct, as they raised and readied their children for emigration, their whole childhood a prelude for another wave goodbye as another ship would grow smaller on waves. *You must speak their way. You will not hunger there.* Most of us in contemporary Ireland had ancestors who survived the famine. It is curious that we do not know neither their names nor their stories, those who stayed on the shore, those who reciprocated countless waves goodbye.

viii. Waves

In Henry Doyle's image, black lines etched over white give us an image of

Ireland so stereotypical that we might prefer to flip the page, to call it it maudlin, sentimental. Easier, always, to disparage art as mawkish, than to dwell on what within us compels us to reject it.

Let us linger a moment with this family, their hands raised in farewell as a ship leaves. The parting is so anguished that the woman has fallen to her knees and covered her face, unable to wave, unable to look. A child buries her face in her father's side. To the left, a young child watches, mimics their wave, a single arm extended towards the boat as it leaves. Her eye is on her sister's arm, mimicking her gesture. Echokinesis.

'Emigrants Leave Ireland', engraving by Henry Doyle (1827–1892)

I am of a people who on finding a lost child might think *Cé leis tú?* but suppress the question, and choose English instead. When I turn that question on myself, the answer comes easily. I belong to a people who feel the past in pangs. I belong to a people who carry a burden in their bones, a shame too terrible to articulate. I belong to a people who choose silence. I belong to a people who wave at waves.

ix. Point

My daughter is in my arms as I extend a finger towards the night sky. Dark, ink-dark, this sky stretching over the Atlantic, and yet a million pinpoints of light burn through. She points too.

We think in English, but in our minds, some fossil of the old language, the old hunger, remains. We might look at a starry night sky, at all those bright cores of hydrogen scorching into helium, and admire their long-dead light. We point upwards and think star but say *stair*, and as we point at the deep starred night, perhaps both of our languages are right.

Each star there shines not as an individual, but nestled into a constellation of its own history, its luminous genealogy. The stars tilt and beckon, pointing back at us. My daughter waves to the sky, and it strikes me suddenly, as the most obvious understandings often do, that she may not be waving goodbye after all. Perhaps this new girl is waving hello.

Weapon of Choice

Susanne Stich

The city, where we used to fly through the night like bats, is a ninety-minute train ride away. How we live now is an assumption, and today will be no exception. At 8.15 sharp I watch Richard leave the house in a freshly ironed suit. He cycles off with his trouser legs clipped to his ankles, and as soon as he's out of sight I change from my pyjamas into my new burgundy dress. I brush my hair, braid it and drape it round my head like a Victorian maid. I put on mascara, open the curtains in every room, then slip into my boots to go and feed our birds. As usual, they make eye contact but stay in the far corner of the aviary, side by side, like Siamese twins. They were already here when we bought the house. About to move abroad, their former owners didn't know what to do with them. Part of me believes these birds understand everything about me. They don't mind my German accent, they get my facial expressions, the rings under my eyes. On top of that, they are lovebirds, the real thing. I watch the sun rise and blend with the southern Cotswolds beyond the stone wall at the far end of the garden. March is nearly over; the birdsong in the nearby forest gravitates towards spring. Our birds love it. Their gentle swaying is almost unnoticeable, but it isn't lost on me, and I have a feeling that this could turn out to be a good day yet.

Back inside I pour myself a glass of water, then switch on the video with the volume up high. There he is, Christopher Walken, in the large, empty hotel, wearing a tired suit and tie. For the umpteenth time he twitches his neck. Before long he dances through endless, mirrored corridors like a bird released. His wedding ring reflects the lights everywhere. In the background, shiny marble floors contrast with garish carpets, rubber trees with poinsettias. He swaggers through massive doors, rings the brass bell at reception. He sways up and down escalators, mounts tables and trolleys with the ease of a cat. Then, in the grand finale he soars through the huge, empty space above the lobby. Suspended from wires deleted in post-production he zips back and forth with signature grace, as if different magnets are competing over him. Finally he's back on his feet, looking both chuffed and a little downhearted. I hit replay just then, don't wait for him to sit down again in the fake antique chair, his head hanging low against the bottle green floor and the blurred vertical blinds. The second and third time around I join in. I always need a little warm-up, but then I, too, dance to 'Weapon of Choice', and as soon as I'm genuinely out of breath I pause the video on a close-up of his face. It's easier to talk like that.

'Christopher,' I say, 'oh Christopher. Can I tell you my story again?'

We've been doing this for three weeks now, and I have a feeling that today there'll be some kind of breakthrough.

'I've known my husband for seven and a half years,' I start, 'we met in a London pub.'

Christopher's eyes widen. It's subtle, but I've got used to it.

'He wanted to act like De Niro,' I continue, 'and I wanted to write novels. But mostly we did other things. I scraped by on a scholarship studying literature, working as a waitress on the side. Richard was trying his luck with casting agencies. When he hit a tight spot financially, his parents stepped in. His father is a retired banker, one of those who received big bonuses long before people talked about them on the news all the time. His mother works for the Royal Opera, she's a milliner. I know…'

At this point Christopher smirks. It's a friendly smirk, and he knows what's coming of course, the sheer scope of my dilemma.

'I'm sorry I only discovered your video last month.'

I say all kinds of things to keep him sweet.

'I remember somebody talking about it when it first came out, but never actually saw it. I've always liked your films, though, the early ones especially.'

There it is, that faint glint in his left eye, practically a nod in my direction.

'Richard's parents smile at everything he does. They smile at me just as much. In the beginning I loved the Englishness of it all. The fact that Richard went to private schools seemed like something from a movie. When I was eleven, my mother and I moved into social housing. My father had died just before I switched to secondary school. He simply dropped dead in the street one day, something he clearly hadn't expected. There was no life insurance policy, no savings. He'd been an accountant, but also, according to my mother, a bit of a gambler.'

Christopher almost shakes his head in disbelief. I take a sip of water.

'My mother had threatened to leave my father over the gambling, but then he was the one who left us. Do you get why I hate numbers?'

This time it's a definite nod.

'I dreamed about speaking English instead, paid attention in school and got the grades. I've been a goody-two-shoes my entire life. My father never travelled anywhere. Like Richard he used to wear suits. He also bought me a budgie once, and then of course he got me a library ticket, oblivious to what it would make of me: an Enid Blyton sucker, a sucker for all things English. Years later, when I met Richard, I worked as a waitress in Leicester Square so I could pay my rent. I smiled and toiled for tips from across the globe.'

The computer screen has gone black. I slide my finger across the touchpad to make him reappear, Christopher, with the same spaced out expression as before.

'Do you want to know how we ended up living here?'

I don't wait for his response. These are the things he needs to get his head around. Repetition won't do any harm.

'Four years into our relationship we were living in a flat Richard's parents had paid for. Like me he's an only child. By then I'd seen him in ads on TV, stage plays and a handful of short films. He was pretty good, but never quite the first choice for the parts he wanted. Over time that got to him. He started having this nightmare about a giant mouse breathing down his neck. He was convinced it meant he didn't have enough talent. Soon after, and without much ado, he gave up acting and decided to be a photographer instead. I'd never seen him take a picture before. His father bought him the best camera on the market. Then, somewhere between the thousands of pictures that followed, we got married. We kept it low-key, invited close friends and family only. It was an overcast day in March, more or less exactly two years ago. There's nothing surprising about a cloudy sky in England at this time of year, but I remember thinking that we should have gone to a place with more sun. Everything suddenly seemed different from what I'd thought it would be. In the lead-up to the wedding, once more, Richard's parents insisted on paying for everything. I didn't like it, refused to let them pay for my dress, and they were okay about it. In fact, they praised my second-hand aubergine-coloured dress as if it were something by Chanel. They smiled all day and I kept thinking about my personal bank balance, how pathetic it was, and how I was marrying into money in an Oxfam dress.'

I take a deep breath and check if Christopher is still listening. He is.

'Anyway, I suddenly felt scruffy-looking at my own wedding, and then, over the course of the day, after years in England, my German accent became really strong. I could hardly string a sentence together. Even my mother, whose

English is minimal, seemed to notice. She shot me these looks all day. Richard's mother had designed a hat for her, which made her look strange, like a spy or something. It wasn't that the hat was ugly or didn't suit her. It suited her very well, in fact, but I had never before seen my mother wear a hat. She stayed close to me all day, her face shiny and a little perplexed.'

Christopher is smirking again.

'Sorry, I'm digressing… About six months after the wedding, around the time of Richard's birthday, he and I began to speak about London as if the city were a person. I can't remember who started it. *She's freaking me out*, Richard said. *It's a he, Richard*, I said, *the city's one hell of an extravagant guy*. We scrawled lists as to why and how we needed the quieter life, but we didn't get anywhere. *I always just see myself sitting at a desk, writing. I can do that anywhere, Richard. But the countryside would be nice.* Yes, I did say stuff like that, and I did worse. To help us with the decision, I told Richard to ring his parents. They'd recently relocated to Somerset because his father had retired.'

I can tell by the sudden change of light on his forehead that Christopher would rather dance again. We do another two rounds of the video. This time I even copy the more difficult moves. Doing all this in a West Country cottage is some feat, but I've been practising of course.

'Before he rang his father about leaving London, Richard procrastinated for nearly a month,' I pipe up again. 'I spent whole days watching him shuffle around our London flat. Eventually he reached for the phone. And within the hour, once again, my father-in-law took his thirty-one-year-old son under his wing. He rang a few contacts and soon found a space for the thing he'd told Richard to do, open a photographer's studio for the wealthy set. A week later he found us this house. Richard's mother said she would help us decorate it. The whole thing was like a painting by numbers prescription, and Richard loved every minute of it. The idea of following parental guidance as a man in his prime was like a new part for him, an unlikely return to acting. I hovered in the background. As always, everybody smiled a lot. The studio opened nine months ago, in the old centre of Bath, a thirty-minute bike ride from our cottage. Richard mostly takes pictures of weddings and babies. *Even August Sander did it*, he says when it bugs him. In the first three months he shrugged a lot.'

I suspect Christopher's smirk is something he was born with. It's not that he's condescending. In fact, I have a feeling it's his way of reassuring me. This guy means business. I move a little closer to the screen, as if I'm about to withdraw a large sum of money, bracing myself to state the exact amount. It'll be good for Christopher to hear me breathe. I too mean business.

'Things became more serious when Richard took to wearing the suits. One day he came home with this large and fancy-looking bag. *They remind me of my father when I was a kid, and, guess what, honey, they're actually quite comfortable*, he said, standing in front of our hall mirror, clad in his new finery. A week later his hairstyle also changed. Suddenly there was a side-parting like a newly paved road along his head. Even then I didn't say anything.'

Christopher looks exhausted, and not in the least bit interested in hearing more. I close the laptop. There's a tightness in my chest. I lie down on the rug in front of the fireplace and look up above me. As a teenager I would have swooned over Cotswold cottage ceilings in general, and this one in particular: the rough plasterwork contrasting with the dark wooden beams, undeniably charming. Why on earth would I want to leave here? To date, telling things to Christopher has been a breeze. I've never told him the entire story, though. I get up, walk past the kitchen basket full of empty glass, and go back into the garden.

I'm the one who recycles our glass. *Vitrics*, Richard sometimes calls it, grinning like a Cheshire cat. When I first heard the word I had to look it up in the dictionary. Leaving that aside, I don't see the connection between empty jars and bottles, and the urge to smile. It's stuff like this that gives me nightmares, the kind I don't remember. Three weeks ago, for instance, I woke up screaming, not having the slightest recollection of a dream. Richard wasn't beside me. I found him in the kitchen, sitting with a strip of banana peel across the table in front of him, his freshly trimmed hair sticking up in all directions.

'Fuck bananas for insomnia. They don't do a bloody thing,' he said when I walked in.

'But you were knackered when you went to bed…'

'Did I just hear you scream?'

I nodded, peeled a banana for myself and went back to bed. There were things in my head I would have liked to say but didn't. They sounded too much like the climactic, final minute of an episode of *Hollyoaks* before *Channel 4 News* comes on. The following morning, however, I danced to the video for the first time, and by noon there was some kind of a thing between Christopher and me.

Then, a fortnight ago, Richard caught me dancing. With my legs split, and my mouth open, I was flying through the double doorframe between our living room and kitchen when he came home early, appearing at my side like a slow-moving wolf, bicycle helmet in hand. Our eyes met, and I blushed like I hadn't in years. Christopher was about to launch himself into the angel bit at the end. Richard looked at me, at the screen, and back at me. He smiled his very loveliest smile, walked into the kitchen, dropped his bag on the floor and filled the kettle.

'Hi,' I whispered, my voice like a leaf in the breeze, and after Richard's usual cup of green tea we made love in front of the fireplace.

It's not all bleak yet, and inside the house, on my laptop screen, behind Christopher's video, there's a half-written article about the promises of spring and the joys of country living.

'With the days stretching, and the scent of the earth becoming more noticeable, we yearn to be outdoors. There are endless opportunities for bringing these sensations into the cottage…' I wrote yesterday.

I must have walked up and down the back garden a dozen times by now. My footprints have left deep marks in the wet ground. The birds are watching my every move. I smirk at them like Christopher, feeling guilty. It's not fair, they don't understand any of this, and it's still early in the day. Richard will be at work for another seven hours. I could drive into Bath, take a walk around Victoria Park, or brush past the tourists on Queen Square, copies of *Pride and Prejudice* sticking out of their pockets. There'll be more of them in the summer, but there always are some. They don't seem to mind that Jane Austen didn't even like this town. In the past, Richard and I joked about stuff like this, and I can't remember when exactly we stopped. The fact that I haven't written a novel is another conundrum. It just so happened that Richard's parents had a few contacts, and before I knew it I found myself penning articles about curtains, staircases and tiles. Considering my background, I have no idea what made me take to it. I spent a few weeks teaching myself the jargon as I walked around antique shops and interior design stores. The magazine people seemed to like what I presented them with.

'You have a different way of looking at things, it's rather charming,' they said. On top of that, seeing my name in print was lovely. Melanie Mason, my English name, sounds like a mysterious, more triumphant version of the one I was born with, strangely at odds with people assuring me that I still look German. I never know what exactly they mean when they say it, and I haven't changed my maiden name with the authorities. For magazine writing purposes, however, I was told that Melanie Stumptner would be a bridge too far.

'Your English is so good, nobody would even suspect you're German,' the first editor said. I left her office feeling chuffed and confused.

'What are you dreaming of, Melanie?' Richard's mother asked me around the same time. It was a grey day, not unlike today, not unlike the wedding day. What I do remember most about her question, though, is that, once I saw the sky, I didn't say the thing I wanted to say: I want to be a lovebird and fly away. Instead, I took my time and noticed how her eyes and Richard's were the same soft brown. Finally I said something about a literary career. It was the next best thing that popped into my head.

'Lovely,' she said, 'let's have some tea.'

My mother-in-law and I have coined a language for ourselves to fill the silences about all the other things: money, children, the past and the future. It's a language not entirely different from birdsong, a lifesaver when it comes to sitting in Richard's parents' light-flooded lounge.

'Why don't you write a bestseller?' she asked when she returned with a tray of designer tea things. Richard didn't come to my defence. He was slouched in an armchair by the door, like a replica of one of his forefathers. My husband knows I'm serious about my writing. I would never set out to write a bestseller. Writing articles about interiors is bad enough.

'You're as stubborn as your father,' my mother used to say, even after he'd died. In fact she's never stopped saying it.

And still, if anyone is up to tackling Richard, it's Christopher, slightly scary American that he is. Against a backdrop of Cotswold stone, he'd cut to the chase and confront Richard about the suit and hair business.

'You're fucking up, Mason. Seriously!'

Richard would walk away with the sense of having experienced some kind of epiphany, I'm sure of it. My husband loves listening to Yanks.

'Go for a spin,' Christopher suggests out of the blue, and, sucker that I am, ten minutes later, changed into my red trench coat and a pair of vintage pumps I bought to remind myself that I can look professional despite working from a cottage boxroom, I pull out of the drive in our Skoda. The sky is the same grey it has been all morning, the street is empty. The kitchen wicker basket is in the passenger seat. I drive slowly to keep the chinking of our Chianti and Malbec empties to a minimum. It's unlikely that I should bump into Richard. He hardly ever leaves his studio. Melanie Mason, here I come.

It's a ten-minute scenic drive into town, even at this time of year, with the trees still bare. The narrow, winding roads, bordered by mansion houses, cottages and endless stone walls, interrupted mostly by evergreens, not to forget the views of Prior Park; all of this taken together never ceases to lift something inside me, some small, crazy thing I cannot explain. I cross the river, turn into the Bath Recycling Centre on Midland Road, park and check my make-up in the mirror. On close inspection the mascara is fine, the lipstick and foundation are not. I'm the worst applier of make-up to walk this earth. I fix it as best I can and scramble out of the car. At the far end of the grounds two men in fluorescent coats wrestle with a mattress. It looks as if it's about to rain. I walk over to the passenger side and slowly lift out the basket. I have a feeling that to the men in the distance it looks like I'm holding a baby. They're staring now. I make the bottles chink a bit, and before I know it I'm catapulting empties into the bottle bank's small opening as if there's no tomorrow. The sound sends shivers up and down my spine. All the shattered pieces, like people in a war, oblivious to the bigger picture that got them there. My eyes fill with tears I haven't felt coming. I stop for a moment, stare into the container opening. It's black in there, hard to make anything out, let alone a single piece of broken glass. I toss the rest of the bottles in with even more force. The tears are running down my face, and with the rain starting, and quickly turning into a downpour, all of this wetness combined feels like the start of a symphony. The men in the distance escape into a portacabin.

'Where will I go next?' I ask, climbing back into the car, my coat and shoes glistening with rain. No answer. The car windows are steaming up. I wipe the windscreen with my palm, start the engine, head towards the Avon and across the bridge. On an impulse I turn right rather than left.

'Home.'

'Sorry, what?' I say and look behind me. The voice sounded familiar. It clearly came from the back seat, but there's nobody there.

'Head home…'

'I don't think I understand…'

'Honey pie, don't act stupid!'

I can't make up my mind whether he sounds nasty or playful, but decide to go with the latter. I'm now on Lower Bristol Road, heading west rather than south where we live.

'I haven't lived in Germany for almost nine years, Christopher. I could never go back. There must be a better way!'

I turn around once more, and there he is, wearing the suit from the video, in the back seat of my Skoda. I almost miss a red light. Had there been a car in front of me I would have crashed right into it.

'There is,' Christopher says, 'there is.'

The lights turn green again. I slowly turn a corner, and there it is, the shop sign: blue and red type on a yellow circle, a blue square behind it. Lidl. People have asked me about its pronunciation many times.

'Liddel?'

'No, Leedl,' I correct them, 'like Leeds, with another l at the end.'

I give Christopher a mournful glance, all set to explain the misery of German supermarkets. He looks utterly disinterested. We pull into the car park all the same.

'Fuck you!' I say, instantly feeling awful, but Christopher's face lightens up.

My parents-in-law love the Christmas sweets Lidl stock from October right into the new year, the nougat marzipan bars and the gingerbread, not to forget the glühwein. They serve them as eccentric treats. In my family we used to go to Lidl because we needed to shop cheaply.

I stay in the car and watch the shop entrance. People come and go almost constantly. They struggle with trolleys, umbrellas, grocery bags. Under a sign detailing the opening hours an old woman unties her little white dog from one of the metal poles. The dog yaps and jumps, but when the woman, who has neither umbrella nor hood, walks out from under the shop's roof, it doesn't budge. I open the window and hear her shout as she pulls the dog towards the rain.

'Oh, Bradley, will you wise up? It's only rain!'

With no immediate response, she hits the dog hard with the lead. This is followed by the briefest of yelps from Bradley, who without further ado follows the woman into the pouring rain, tail held high.

'Good boy,' she praises and walks off.

If this is home, I'd rather be dead. I don't need anything from Lidl. I shop ahead, the fridge is full, it's only Tuesday. If I go in, chances are I'll get seduced by the tables with special offers: underwear, notebooks, fluffy towels. If there are wellington boots, as there sometimes are, and I guess it's that time of year, I could buy a pair for Richard so he'd step into the garden with me. For a moment, the thought of it is comforting, but the realisation that he wouldn't wear them comes crashing down like Bradley's lead. Richard would merely smile; the boots would go straight to landfill, he's ruthless that way. He might even say something like, 'If you want, honey, we'll get a gardener.'

'Did you see Bradley?' I whisper without turning around. 'Poor little sod of a dog.'

Part of me still imagines a happy ending. I could leave the car right here and walk into town. There's a golf umbrella in the boot. Fast walker that I am it would take me less than half an hour. I could surprise Richard in his studio, set off the old-fashioned doorbell. He'd be at the counter in his freshly ironed suit.

'What a rare surprise,' he'd say.

'Yes.'

'Are the birds okay?'

Our birds always seem to worry Richard. They never worry me; I just love them, and that's something I would not have expected to say about myself, that I have a genuine love of birds.

'Of course,' I'd assure him.

'Are you?'

To this, regardless of my husband's polite emphasis, I wouldn't respond, because, to be honest, I'm not sure what exactly is wrong with me.

'Were you with Christopher Walken again?' he'd ask next.

'My little secret,' I'd say.

'I take it that's a yes.'

'He's in the back seat of our car at Lidl car park.'

'Liddel car park?'

'Leedl car park, yes.'

If I were writing a suicide note today, it would read something like this: *Sincere apologies to everyone, but Melanie is a fool. She's been labouring under a misapprehension for a long, long time. Wearing red didn't serve her. There are novels inside of her like broken bottles. Other than her ignorance she has no excuse. Please cremate her and spread her ashes as you see fit.*

I guess one way of continuing with the day a little less dramatically would be to ask Christopher how many more innocuous conversations he thinks my marriage can take.

'Do you fancy going into the shop with me?'

That's an easier question to start with.

'We could make a grand entrance, tango past the sales tables, look for leftover marzipan,' I say. 'It's been three weeks, you and me! Perhaps we could crank things up a bit, let the world know or something…'

I open the car door, grateful for the cold, wet air. Christopher climbs out and follows me, good man that he is. I take his hand, and there we are, heading into Lidl.

Aunt Libby

watches sea mist fall like silk from the sky's shoulders,
the last star slip—a distracted child—
from dawn's open hand.

Trees are shedding versions of themselves,
throwing leaves to the flames
that flicker like squirrels across the graveyard

where last night Aunt Libby ran
flapping those impertinent cloths.
She knows the anguish

of having your purpose questioned,
of needing to be fought for.
She knows what palliative care only means.

The scholars and dustmen are here again
listing in their ledgers and scrolls
what she eats and when and in how many ways

she's been useful. Aunt Libby mistakes useful
for beautiful. She calls them her *poor little mites,*
blows smoke rings into their faces.

Leaning from her conspiratorial bed—
she won't sit in the day room because
she refuses *to be like them*—

she says she's been good as gold
since they scraped all the wasps from her brain
and that horse started ploughing

a backwards path through the model village
where visitors come and go
like memories ripped or sold or slaughtered.

Aunt Libby says she'll stay
as long as her books are within reach
and there's enough light to read them by.

Tess Jolly

Legacy

My mother took us picnicking on trains
to see rosebay willowherb dance
along the track. On wet days
her Coddington magnifier
made us fluent in the sex life of flowers,
the symmetry of petals, the margins of leaves.
No unkempt laneway where we marched
behind her sensible bottom
was complete without a lesson
on the tiny heads and beaks of cranesbill
or the leguminous links
between vetch and peas.
When the sky was harebell-blue
and skylarks rose on threads of song,
we treasure-hunted through summer sandhills
for drumsticks of purple orchid.

Something is creeping through her memory now
like spreading tendril roots of buttercup,
so bird's-foot trefoil might be gorse,
thrift is a pink flower, woodruff white.
I still spot coltsfoot before its leaves appear
and rub wild thyme between my finger tips.
My children know how to suck nectar from fuchsia heads,
that cuckoos don't make cuckoo spit.
They show her the shine of sunlit celandine
among yellow flags in a wet field
and when she asks, I say the words she knew—
oxeye, plantain, lady's mantle,
bugle, cowslip, bladderwort,
speedwell, Mum, forget-me not.

Sharon Flynn

Slow Puncture

Shaving blade wrapper flutters to the ground
revealing silky glints in teenaged hands.
Silver bicycle angles against sunlit wall,
leaning well back from the world;
gleaming frame sharp as any blade.

Fuchsia surrounds the garden; splatter-fest suspended,
dripping red in afternoon air, waiting
its moment to drop a curdling mass of blood.
Winged insects flit and buzz that hemmed-in tune
of small creatures seeking safe passage elsewhere.

The boy with the blade shuffles on yellow runners
through uncut lawn. Daisies bow before him.
He slumps to the grass under the maple tree.
Rigid bark takes weight of shoulders
razor sharp with edgy reminders.

He sits with eyes for mocking gnomes that peep
from a nettled world of banged-out rockery.
On a garden seat his schoolbag sags, life battered from it
by boots of thugs. The bike continues to tilt against
the empty cottage, frame grey now clouds have come.

Cheerless ashen colour matches the mood in his head,
sharp tint of metal in his hand. He fingers the blade,
wondering if his father needs it for the morning.
A leafy blade helicopters to the ground beside the bike's
front wheel. He gives the *Raleigh* a last departing look.

Those wheels rescued him today and many times but tomorrow
where would they swoop on him with taunts and spits and digs?
The boy feels nothing at first, human skin punctured
in an invisible way that fails to register with the brain.
That small slit in the fabric of his body drains

like air from a nicked tube. He cannot bear to see
where the puncture is and possesses no means to patch it.
The second slashing feels pricklier than the first.
A slow air of desperation clings to him like silent hisses
in clammy, leaking wrists. The sun comes out again.

He leans back against the tree, feeling no more harshness;
in its ridges sturdiness, softness, a welcome embrace.

David Murphy

Rustlers
Michael Nolan

I was turfed in the back with nothing but a toolbox to sit on. There were wee drawers full of screws that rattled as the van went, and it went all right. My da drove like a demon, chucking me left and right through every dip and turn. 'I need a piss,' I called, but he couldn't hear. I stood up, put my mouth to the gap in the chip-wood panel between the front and back and told him I was bursting.

'You've a bottle in there,' he shouted. 'Piss in the bottle.'

The two-litre bottle of coke was half-empty and flat, so I stood up and undid my jeans. It was a rigmarole with the van belting round corners and me clawing out for something to hold on to while targeting my purple helmet in the hole and squeezing a drip. Ended up wetting my hand, but still near filled the bottle, the piss going a funny shade of black mixed in with the coke.

We stopped in a narrow lane with trees hanging down. The door slid open, hitting me with glary morning light sore in the eyes. My da was standing in boots and weather-all's like he was ready to storm a beach. 'Do you need to go?' he said.

I said I did and hopped out.

There were more fields, trees cuffing the fields and shabby looking hedges, a house across the way. One of those houses you see in the country with a pointy roof and slab-grey walls. I took myself out of my jeans and thought this is where we're supposed to be. But I couldn't see any sheep, not in that field or the one beyond where mist smudged the grass. A breeze tickled. I gave myself a nip.

'Watch out for them birds,' Bimbo shouted, twiddling his baby finger at me. He was cooped up in the passenger seat with the door hanging open. The van tilted down with the weight of him. He'd been my da's mate since before I was spat out and he got on like this was something he had over me. My da paced with his phone to his ear, his head tilted as if to hear.

'We're on the lane,' he was saying. 'We said nine o'clock. If these culchie bastards catch a whiff of us we're chinned.'

I sat on the ground with my back against a tree and stayed well clear. My da took his rustling seriously. Him and Bimbo were at it flat out every Sunday, and I was forever getting roped in because I stayed with him at the weekends and hadn't a choice. Sure what else would I be doing? Playing football? Throwing stones at lampposts?

The cow shite was the worst. The stink was everywhere and had me heaving. Bimbo didn't give a fiddlers. He sat there munching crisps, his greasy fingers burrowing into the bag. 'Gimme one,' I said, and he flicked me the finger. 'Go ahead. Just one.'

I didn't even want one. I was bored to the bollocks and trying to get a reaction from him. He slapped a handful into his mouth and offered the bag.

'There's nothing in it,' I said.

Bimbo grinned potato-pasted teeth and dropped it to the ground.

'Magill's going to meet us farther on,' my da said, slipping his phone in his pocket and pulling the side door open.

'Farther on where?' Bimbo said.

'Down the road. Get in the back, Gavin. We're going.'

I stayed where I was. My da wasn't much taller than me, but he was stocky and strong with shoulders that could charge a bull. He held the door open like he would for a lady, and I could see into the back; the manky floor cluttered with wire coils and carpet and the toolbox I'd spent half the morning wrestling to hold on to. For a mad moment I wanted to fight him.

Few more years, I thought, and patted the dust from my arse.

We met the fella Magill on another lane. There was a jeep parked up with a trailer big enough for horses, and Magill standing by with his country arms crossed. He was big and bald and looked at me with a gammy tilt of the head.

'I need you to give me a hand,' my da told me. 'Bimbo's back's playing up.'

Magill swiped gravel with a laced boot and stared.

'It's heavy, so be easy,' my da said, bending down to pull the trailer from the tow bar. 'Ready?'

I said I was, but the sudden unsteady weight caught me snoozing. My feet slid on the stones and Magill smirked.

'Wee bit to the left, Gavin. That's it. Take your time.'

I'd a good grip, but the bar was cutting the hands off me even though my da was taking most of the weight. I could feel it lighter on my side and was mortified. He swung the trailer round like it was nothing.

'That's us,' he said, hooking it to the van. I let go and checked the red lines carved across my palms.

'No messing about now,' Magill said. 'It needs to be done early.'

'What time does he leave?'

'Ten. He does the milk round.'

My da said happy days and they talked prices. The fields around us were hilly. Still it smelled of shite, a wet sludgy smelling shite that stinks your clothes for a week. My da would drop me home that night and my ma would look at me, disgusted, and kick me into the shower. 'Where's he had you?' she'd say, and I'd be tempted to tell.

Magill got into his jeep and farted back down the lane. My da stared. People said we looked like each other. We'd the same dark hair and eyes, and we both raised our eyebrows when we were talking like we were trying to see over glasses neither of us wore. Sometimes my ma would look at me and gasp, and I'd feel an awkward flush of pride.

'You all right?' he asked.

Before I could answer, Bimbo stuck his vending machine head out the window. 'Any chance? There isn't a sheep in sight and Gavin's mooching for a tussle, aren't you, kid?'

We drove along roads that were more like dirt tracks than roads, and it took us half the morning to find the place. By the time we did, my arse was aching from trying to stay on the toolbox without face-planting the floor. We pulled up by a gate on a leaky back road bordered with bushes, and got out.

It was ewes we were after, these ones with black faces staring across the field like burglars in balaclavas. We leaned on the gate with our elbows at our chins. My da was chewing at the bit to get going. 'We'll go left round the side of the field,' he was saying. 'Cut back across and filter them this way.'

Bimbo spat stringy gobs and joked about throwing a few woolly ones in the back with me. Then it was quiet. We were in the blunt-end of nowhere. The sky domed out and the stillness hung. The farmer's house was a few fields over. It was a big gaff with two chimneys and windows you could swim in. The car was still in the drive and I wondered how he'd react when he came home to find half his flock gone. The insurance will cover it, my da always said, and that the sheep were being raised for slaughter. If anything we were doing the fluffy friggers a favour, and their dopey-headed faces hadn't a clue.

My da straightened up. The car was pulling out of the drive. Too far away to hear, some sheep turned their skulls and chewed. 'That's us,' he said.

We broke the lock and opened the gate wide, pulled the trailer round and set the ramp down. There were a few testy baas. One looked at me like I'd dumped in its garden. My da was whispering, 'there now. Good and slow, lads. Take her easy.'

A big mummy sheep came tearing forward, and stopped. We moved slowly towards them, me and Bimbo fanning to each side while my da spread his arms like a preacher. The sheep started backpedalling. They never knew what to be at when we came for them like this. They bunched up with worried eyes and put me in mind of fish in a tank; when they moved their wool puffed and they could've been floating.

'Easy now,' my da said.

We had them yards from the gate. They were bumping into each other trying to find a way between us; we closed in fast. They panicked and squealed and made a run for it. Some squeezed between the gate and road while others got halfway up the ramp and took a tumble in the tussle. Black legs buckled like burnt matchsticks and we were there, grabbing muckles of clumpy wool and shoving them in.

We got the trailer closed and locked. The road was clogged with sheep babbling between the hedges. 'That's the ticket,' my da said, while Bimbo held his knees and coughed to catch his breath. I slapped his back.

'You all right, fat boy?'

He spat between his feet, too puffed out to speak.

'C'mon,' my da said. 'We need to split.'

I held onto the toolbox under me as the bottle of piss-coke rolled across the floor. The rush had me giddy. We had at least twenty, and we were like bandits tearing across the country. It would get even better when we sold the sheep and my da laughed his whooping laugh and slipped me a few quid to keep me sweet. I listened to Bimbo and him bantering in the front and wished I was sitting between them, all three of us buzzing off each other with the sheep in the trailer wondering what the hell had just happened.

Then we stopped. The front doors screeched and closed with a crack. My heart slipped. I tried to open the side door and it was locked. 'What's happening?' I said, and didn't get an answer. I tried to see into the front and couldn't make anything out. There were voices, and I imagined my da running one way and Bimbo the other; me left in the van surrounded by silver Skodas. I banged the door.

'Daddy. Daddy, where are you?'

The door skimmed open. My da looked flustered. 'I need you to stay here and mind the van,' he said.

We were parked on a road at the back of the farmer's house we'd just done over. There was a field between us and it, and the heady musk of hedges hung in the heat. 'No way,' I said. 'I'm not staying here.'

I was scundered red and not for letting him see. He glanced at the ground, then at me hunched under the roof. I hadn't called him Daddy in years. The guilt was in his gammy face and I felt bad for it.

'We have to be quick,' he said, and stepped back to let me out.

We made across the field like mercenaries. The grass squelched and we kept low, dodging the breeze that cupped the field and the trees all around it. Bimbo was panting behind me, and when we got to the bushes and forced our way through the sticky smelling branches, he had to stop.

'I'm gonna puke.'

We pushed through to the back garden. A gnome was fishing in a pond and there was a swing set by the shed, a football net in front of the stables, and all sorts of dainty looking flowers snuggled up to the house. My da tried the back door and was surprised to find it locked. 'Look,' he said, and pointed to the conservatory. One of the windows was hanging open.

He climbed through, knocking an ornament of a woman in a dress to the floor. I glanced back towards the van, but couldn't see it through the bushes that were smattered with sun. 'You scared?' Bimbo said. I told him nah, and he looked at my legs as if he could see them shaking.

The back door opened and my da was there, beaming. In we went, through the kitchen and into the hall. Our footsteps echoed. That's how big it was. They echoed. The floors were wooden and glossed to a sheen, and a glittery looking chandelier dangled above us.

'Keep dick, Gavin,' my da said, pointing to the front room.

Him and Bimbo headed upstairs and I did what I was told. The curtains hung to the floor, and I could see to the end of the driveway and nothing much else. You'd think a farmer would have a humble wee gaff with a sitting room and a fireplace and a few scenic paintings on the walls. Maybe you'd catch a whiff of boots, or dog, but not here. It smelt of leather and dusty picture frames and made me think of a library. The ceiling couldn't be reached with a brush pole, and there was a piano in the corner by the bookshelves. A music book on the stand was opened at the page of a tune called 'Für Elise'. It made me uneasy. They were taking ages upstairs. I was about to call up when my da came waltzing into the room, his neck hanging with gold necklaces that blinked in the early morning light simpering through the window. He'd a rucksack full of stuff slung over his shoulder, a paddy cap on his head. 'What do you reckon?' he said, puffing his chest out like a man in a portrait. Then he took the hat off and slapped it on me. 'There you go. Farmer Gavin.'

Bimbo stomped in with another rucksack and they looked around the room, but nothing tickled their fancy. 'We need to head on,' Bimbo said.

'What about the stables?'

'Fuck the stables. We've enough.'

My da checked the time. He wasn't ready to give over. 'Yous two take the stuff back to the van and I'll meet yis there.'

'I'll stay with you,' I said.

He handed Bimbo his rucksack and I waited on him to say no, but he didn't. When we got outside, Bimbo lumbered his way towards the bushes and I followed my da to the stables. It was only when we got close that I heard a radio playing classical music. The stables had been divided into pens and there were dogs in each of them; black Labradors that danced on their hind legs and stuck their snouts through the railings for a sniff.

'No good,' my da said, then stopped at the last cage and clapped. The dogs loved this and howled. 'Is there a lead?' he said, before spotting one hanging by the door and grabbing it.

I didn't feel right about this. I glanced towards the house, then at the football net in the garden making shadows on the grass. A breeze groomed the flowers and the gnome at the pond was blushing. My da opened the cage and a border collie stepped out, smiling. 'Look at him,' he said. 'He's a cracker, isn't he?'

I heard a gentle crunching sound and thought it was the radio. My da was scratching the collie's chin. 'This fella's going to make our job a lot easier,' he said.

I peeked out of the stable and saw a car mowing across the driveway.

'Daddy,' I said, and hated myself.

He heard it too. He straightened up and shushed me. 'Wait,' he whispered, and stood with his back against the wall to see out. When he looked at me again and saw my face, he nearly choked. 'It's all right,' he said. 'Take it easy.'

He turned away like he couldn't cope. The dog stood by him and I was raging at his giddiness, and the dog's happy obedience, and my own humiliating panic. I wanted to lock myself in a cage and pray to God the farmer would feel sorry for me when he found me. My da was in kinks laughing. 'You're pale as a plate,' he said, and covered his mouth with his hand.

The engine knocked off. A woman on the radio was wailing her lungs out. Tails slapped the ground.

'Soon as he goes into the house we bolt for the van, right?' my da said.

'Right,' I said, and as soon as the word left my mouth, we heard the gentle click of a door closing and were away like stink.

The collie bounded between us, its tongue loping out the side of its mouth as we broke through the bushes and into the field. The necklaces were still clattering about my da's chest as I held the beak of my Paddy cap and hoped the farmer wouldn't have the sense to look out the window and see us bailing across the bleached grass towards the van where Bimbo had the engine started.

I dove into the back and the dog leapt in with me. The door slammed and we hammered up the road the way we came, left onto another road so crooked and rutted the dog was struggling to keep its feet. He looked at the drawers full of screws like he couldn't understand why they made such a racket. We were tossed up and down and the trailer full of sheep hurdled along behind. I couldn't see us getting away with it, yet we were. The jittery potholed roads soon gave way to tarmac. We were on the motorway. My da and Bimbo were giving it stacks in the front while I cuddled the shaky dog between my legs.

I checked its collar. His name was Butch.

We drove for so long Butch boked on the floor and it smelt like something pulled from a hole. I scratched him behind the ear and he tilted his head and sighed. Every time I stopped, he'd nudge my hand with his soppy nose and rest his chin on my thigh. He was always smiling, even while he boked, and kept looking at me like he was mine. I didn't know how to tell him he wasn't.

I tried to sleep but my stomach was going bucko. I couldn't be sick. It would only give my da something else to laugh at. He'd look at Butch's sick and my sick and chuckle at my luck. So I gulped and breathed. My ma swore by breathing in your nose and out your mouth, and the thought of my ma made me sore.

When we got to where we had to go, my da let me out and I plonked myself on the ground. We were by the sea, and the grass was dusty with sand. The fields sloped down to the water and the water was blue to the horizon. Behind us was a cottage, and beyond that were fields and cattle in the fields. No trees. Barely a bush. Only the road we came from, and the green fields under the sky.

I sat with my legs crossed watching Butch sniffing and pissing every few steps. My da and Bimbo looked into the back of the van and winced at the stink.

'Jesus Christ,' Bimbo said. 'What'd you eat?'

My da got wipes, climbed into the back and started dabbing. I don't know why him and my ma broke up. I was too young when it happened for anything to be made of it. All my ma ever said was, 'he's your da, and I'll not stop you from seeing him.' Like it wasn't up to her. Even when he forgot to pick me up from school and I had to sit at the gates with a teacher I could tell was mooching to get home. Or when he ditched me in his flat until stupid o'clock in the morning, then came wailing in the door with a woman in heels that scraped the floor.

He dropped the sick-stained wipes out onto the grass. Bimbo stood by chewing a straw from a carton of juice he'd guzzled just before. 'Some craic that was,' he said. 'Never seen your da run so fast in my life.'

My da was on his knees in the back of the van, face still pinched with the smell. He told Bimbo to go see the fella down the road. The bald fella who gave us the trailer. Magill. He was leaning with his back against a gate, watching us.

Bimbo went on his way. Butch followed with a curious wiggle, and my da was stuck with me. An uncertain bleat quavered from the trailer. My da went to the passenger side door and got some air freshener, sprayed it in the back and stuck his head in to make sure the sickly smell was gone. Then he trudged round to the driver's seat and hoked about for something. When he came back, he stood with his hands buttered to his pockets like he didn't know what to do.

'So do you like the dog?' he said.

I said I did, and he asked me what I wanted to call it. 'His name's Butch,' I said. 'He's got a collar.'

'Sure that doesn't matter. You can call him anything you want.'

'You can't just change his name. That's not how it works.'

'But he's your dog now.'

'No he's not. He's not coming home with me, is he?'

I sounded more dramatic than I'd meant to, but stealing sheep was one thing, this was someone's dog. My da took a step back. He hadn't a clue how we'd gotten onto this. Neither had I, yet it seemed more important than anything.

'Your ma wouldn't have a dog,' he said, like she was to blame. 'But sure you'll see it at the weekends, won't you?'

'I don't want to do this anymore.'

His face softened and he bent down beside me. 'That's okay,' he said. 'Don't worry. Sure you can come stay with me on a Friday and I'll drop you home on the Sunday morning. That would work all right, wouldn't it?'

I shrugged and said it would, not knowing how to say what I was trying to say.

'Don't get me wrong,' he said. 'I'll be gutted not having you with me. You're good at the rustling. But if it's not what you want to do it's okay. We can work round it.'

I knew he was trying to make everything better, but I felt like I was taking a weight off his shoulders. Bimbo called out. He was coming up the road with Butch strutting by his side like his work for the day was done. My da straightened up. 'That's us,' he said. 'Come on. We did good. A wee smile would go down a treat.'

He poked me in the ribs, playfully pulled the Paddy cap down to my eyebrows. I slapped his hand away. 'Stop it,' I said.

I hit his hand with more force than I meant to and he looked hurt, then torn, like he couldn't decide if he should shout at me, or apologise.

Instead, he left me sitting there and went back to the van. Him and Bimbo got in. Butch ran alongside them trying to chew the wheels as they reversed down the road. There was nothing else to look at. The land was flat and green and quiet. It was no different from anywhere I'd seen before, yet I felt weirdly alone. I watched them climb out of the van and say a few words to Magill. Butch was put on his lead and the trailer doors pulled open.

For a second, I thought the trailer was empty and that the sheep had disappeared. I could imagine my da's face paling and Bimbo's stupid mouth falling open, them both turning to me like I had something to do with it. I wished that I had. I could've left the trailer open and let the sheep tumble out as we made our escape down the motorway. They'd bounce between cars like fleecy pinballs causing all sorts of havoc as my da drove on, clueless.

But the sheep hadn't gone anywhere. Out they came with their coats all scraggly, hobbling down the ramp and across the field on woozy legs. I could hear my da's voice. He was on his tiptoes pointing things out to Magill. He patted Bimbo on the shoulder like he couldn't have done this without him, and I made up my mind. I didn't want to see him anymore. The next weekend he phoned, I'd tell my ma I didn't want to speak to him. I'd tell her the same thing the weekend after and the weekend after that until he stopped calling and I didn't have to listen to him at all.

When the sheep were in the field and the gate was locked, the van came hankering up the road to get me. The windscreen was glazed white in the brightness, and I could just about make out the shape of my da at the wheel and Bimbo stuffed into the passenger seat. Then I saw a little head; Butch squeezed between them squinting in the sun. The horn beeped. 'Hurry up,' Bimbo said, but I wasn't for moving. He said something to my da and my da got out and came round the front of the van. His face was dripping. He wiped the sweat from his eyes with the back of his arm and pulled the side door open.

'Have you coke left? I'm choking for a drink.'

'Behind the toolbox,' I told him, and he knelt in and lifted the bottle that had darkened in colour and cooled in the shade. He looked at me as he unscrewed the lid. Bimbo watched, and Butch sat on his lap and watched with him. I stayed where I was. The breeze lapped my ears. Somewhere at the other side of the road, a ewe bleated. My da held the bottle to his lips, expecting me to stand up. I could smell the sea. It smelt like piss.

I waited.

Cork

Old Cork was more the unconscious
in concrete. It was more the Palaeozoic
parts of us: darkly lit, dingy, dirty
physical parts of who we are, with peat bogs
ectopically on top of rooftops, the locale like
the body of a man running amok
and being a greaseball all over town.

I remember nineteen eighty-four as a swamp:
herringbones of unlit alleyways with men
in mussed wigs mullocking up poulaphoukas
of boreens, and the river non compos mentis
brimmed with flâneurs foot-sucking their way up Pana
with bullfrogs and pram-carts in a place
that was the psychological equivalent

of a mullet hair-cut on a person—it could stand
a serving of psychology's shadow side: the
showbands' hucklebucking tone-deaf, bodacious
bandwagon chummed-with behind the persona's back,
psychotic contracts with the banshee and phouka
conceded to in matters of land, and religion's
piscatorial Christ caught off Pope's Quay

on a Friday, served with the contents
of the chip-pan. We could pride ourselves on the appalling
creation of conscience in the smithy
of *The Late Late Show*, be secretly stricken
by our sinful Saturdays at the dogs,
and hoors shaving our blessedness to a measly aureole
of onion rings. Now Cork is more like a fella

thinking too much, smells nicer
than he is, nicer than he should do,
than we are. Waking up in a bone
china shop, and is careful (but living
on the fragile summit of a swarm),
and proudly feels small enough to give himself airs:
his tipples of Cointreau, his (spat-in) canapés.

Kevin Cahill

A Foreign Country

Black bees / white noise
in the hollow trunk
of the old plane tree
below my window;

everything here so
familiar / unfamiliar,
or is it that I have forgotten
the way moonlight

can skewer the bedroom
through a shutter crack,
the crepitation of tyres
over sand-crush and pebbles,

the discreet / indiscreet dawn
departure of a lover, the illusion
of being unseen, thinned dark
poor cover when dogs snarl

as they doze and a streak of
black cat sleeks from under
the gangling lavender, un-
leashes a memory,

an out-of-body déjà-vu,
impossible to capture
from the widening delta
of the past.

Geraldine Mitchell

Dogs

Jennifer Down

Usually we took turns but sometimes Foggo wanted her to himself. Once he called it, that was it.

Foggo had the car, so he was the boss. It belonged to his dad, but his dad was dead. Foggo was also the biggest, though Willy was catching up. Everyone thought of Foggo as the biggest, anyhow.

China wasn't Chinese. His mum was Malaysian or Maltese or something. His dad was Vietnamese, and everyone knew he made drugs. Speed and E. There was a weird thing where China didn't talk about it, and none of us had ever seen Mr T at work, but everyone knew. It wasn't just the kids. All the parents said it, too.

Nicky was the smallest but he had the most to say. He had this way of cracking you up just by looking at you. I reckon he was the smartest of the lot of us, but he never let on.

Willy's family had a dishwasher and an Xbox. His parents taught at the Catho school. He was the sort of kid who used to be scrawny and cop shit for it, and then he got bigger and won best and fairest three years in a row.

On Fridays we'd pull up outside the pub and the girls'd be standing outside waiting for us. You could have your pick. Foggo would drive by and look at them all huddled there, like a police line-up, smoking and touching their hair. If he didn't see anything he liked he'd bite his thumbnail and say, *dogs, fucken dogs, mate,* and we'd all agree, and we'd roar out of there. On to Maccas or the river or someone's house, if we knew there was something going on.

The trophies were China's idea. I didn't really get it. It wasn't like we ever looked at them. Mostly they went in the console or the glove box, but a few things—like Casey Grimes' gold necklace with the cross, or one of those detachable bra straps we think came from Steph Horsburgh—a few things, we hung from the rearview mirror. The gold cross creeped me out. It was only the size of a five-cent coin, but at night it glinted under street lights.

I also thought it was weird that none of the girls ever asked for her shit back. Like, maybe Courtney Wyatt didn't care she'd left her undies on the back seat of Foggo's dead dad's car, or maybe she was too embarrassed. But I was always surprised about Casey's necklace. She went to school with Willy's sister. I saw her around a bit after that night we took her for a ride, but I never saw her with another cross. Probably her mum or dad gave it to her. Shit like that made me feel bad, but it wasn't the sort of thing you could say to the other guys.

I used to think we never did it with girls who didn't want it, but one time there was a chick said we'd forced her. 'Chicks are like that,' Fog said. 'They feel bad afterwards, so they try to make it better for themselves.' That's what my dad told Mr Wye when we all got called into his office after school that time. Willy's dad was mad as a cut snake, but the rest of the dads just laughed. China's old man didn't even show. It was stinking hot that day. I remember the wormy track of sweat down the side of Mr Wye's head. Afterwards we rode down to the river. Something must've spooked us a bit, because none of us spoke till we were there. Then Fog laid down his bike and said, 'She wanted it,' and we all went, *Yeah*, and Fog said, 'Fat cunt. Just about had to roll her in flour to find the wet spot,' and we all said the way we remembered it till we were sure it was right.

Foggo had this way of testing us. When we skated he'd get us to do bigger and bigger tricks. He wasn't the best at it—Nicky was—but he had no fear. When we started getting over skating, since none of us could do that many tricks anyway, he began to light the ramps on fire. He'd pour petrol in a ring on the ground, or dribble it in a line along the concrete benches in the park where we used to try darksliding.

He made things more exciting just when we were getting bored. Like one time I was dumb enough to tell China I thought Despina Vasilakis was hot. He told Foggo. One night we're all drinking on the oval and Fog pulls up with Desi in the car. We all sit around on the cricket pitch. For some reason we've got extra grog, and we've done some nangs, and we're all fucked. Desi's sitting across from me. I can hardly look at her, she's that beautiful. Her breath comes out in clouds. She's got half a smile on her face like she's waiting for the end of a joke. She whinges once or twice about the cold, and finally Willy gets a tarp from the car to put around her. Whenever she reaches for the bottle she makes a plasticky rustling sound. When Fog starts kissing her I'm pissed, but I know I'm gunna get my turn, so I'm waiting. Thing is, Desi's hard work. She's drunk and real floppy. Once she even spews everywhere—mostly on herself and on the tarp, but Foggo's lucky he gets out the way in time. When it's my turn her face is pressed to the grass, in her own spew. I've got two fingers in and she's not even looking at me. She's making this whiny noise. The guys are watching and I can't get hard. I have to get myself going. Fog and Nicky are pissing themselves. When I finally come it's a relief. Desi probably won't remember it but I won't forget it, because I really wanted to do it different with her.

She had frizzy dark hair that she made straight, but there were always these little fluffy baby hairs round her forehead. Killer legs and this huge smile. Now when I think of her, it's Bundy vomit and blue tarp. After school she moved to Melbourne to go to uni. She was really smart. Her undies were white with a satiny yellow rosebud, smaller than my fingernail, on the front. China nicked the flower. He hooked it into the clip of the bra strap. Seeing it made me feel crook, so after a while I put it in the glove box with some of our other stuff.

The last time it happened there was nothing for us to keep. Foggo, Nicky and I were cruising, waiting for Willy to finish work, waiting for China to answer the phone. We parked out the front of the bottle shop. Foggo went in. Nicky and I waited underneath the lit-up sign. Nicky kicked at the pebbles. His fidgeting drove me mental. I watched Foggo talking to the guy behind the counter.

He came out holding the plastic bags. A lot of Jimmy, a pack of cigarettes, plus whatever else he'd stuffed down his pants. He held out his hand for money. I looked over his shoulder at the guy behind the counter. He waved at me. I didn't wave back.

'I got an idea,' Foggo said. He sounded like he did after one of his crazy sprints up the guts, kicking one on the fly from outside fifty. He was fast for a big guy. 'You wait here. I'll be back. Tell Willy we'll meet him at the park.'

'What one?'

'Fuck, Nicky, the one near the airfield. The one we fucken always go to, you dumb cunt.'

'How the fuck's Willy gunna get there?' I asked.

Foggo shrugged. He opened the car door, stood with a hand on top. 'Just tell him to meet us. It'll be a surprise.'

'At least give us some durries to have now, cunt,' Nicky said. Foggo threw him the whole pack, then pitched two tinnies at me. He chucked them overarm out the car window so hard I almost dropped them. The car roared off and I thought, *He'll get pinged by the cops.*

We walked up the road to the payphone and called Willy. He was just finishing his shift at the IGA. Marissa Markovic answered the phone and Nicky chewed her ear off so long I had to put in another forty cents. I heard her laughing down the line. We walked back to the bottle-o car park and started to drink. Nicky was talking shit. He got up and started to pace a bit, toeing at the pebbles below the lit-up sign again. I said, 'Fuckssake, Nicky, can you keep still. You got a worm or something?' He just laughed.

'Can't help it,' he said. The white bits of his eyes were shining. He was hopping from one foot to the other now. 'What, you gotta take a piss, mate? Fog's gunna love that, fucken ballet dance.'

'Stop tryna be him, cunt,' Nicky said. But we grinned at each other. I liked Nicky even when he was a pain in the arse.

We'd finished half the pack of cigarettes by the time Foggo got back. I heard his car ages before I saw it, hole in the muffler. He pulled in by the bottle shop. He stuck his head out the window.

'Fuck you been?' Nicky called.

'Had to go to the servo,' said Fog. He was doing a smile that made him look nuts. China was sitting next to him. I stomped my empty can of Jimmy and yanked open the passenger door. Willy's sister was in the back. She was still in her striped school dress and rugby jumper. I saw she'd pulled the sleeves down over her fingers.

'Where's Will,' she said. She looked right at me. White-blue light on her, the kind of light that shows up your veins. I got a bad feeling in my guts. I tried to make my face say sorry.

'Settle down, Missy,' Foggo said. 'I told you already. He's gunna meet us.'

'I don't believe you,' she said. Her voice was like cut glass.

Fog looked at her in the rearview mirror. He raised his shoulders. 'All right. Don't.' He turned to me. 'You gunna get in, or just stand there?'

I got really mad then. She wasn't even the sort Foggo liked—big tits, big bum. Girls that looked like women. Missy was tall but narrow, like there were parts of her that didn't realise they were supposed to grow. She kept her nails short for netball. And she was too young to hang out the front of the pub. Fog was only doing it to fuck with Willy.

'Fog,' I said. 'This is fucked.'

'I don't care if you're gunna be a pussy, but either get in or don't,' Foggo said.

'You going or not?' Nicky said to my shoulder blades. I walked around to the passenger side and opened the door. China got out with a shitty look on his face and slid in the back, and Nicky followed. Missy was pressed right up against the window like she couldn't get far enough away from either of them. China passed her a tin, but she wouldn't take it.

'He's just being friendly,' Fog said. He was still watching in the rearview mirror. The gold cross was spinning and sending off points of light.

'Where are we meeting Will?' Missy asked.

'He's being friendly,' Fog said again. 'No need to be a bitch about it.'

He pumped the pedal so fast my neck snapped back, hit the part of the seat where the headrest should've been. He saw. He smirked. I wanted to kill him.

Willy was already there when we got to the park. I saw his mum's car, which he wasn't meant to borrow on Friday nights. Fog rolled down his window, revved the engine.

'We going to the airport?' Willy called. He didn't even look in the back seat. Fog gave him a thumbs-up and floored the accelerator again. Willy's lights flicked on and he followed us up the road. The airfield was closed for the night. They'd re-fenced it all about three years before. Used to be you could only get in if you climbed through a hole in the cyclone wire, but then one time we brought equipment and cut the padlocks on the side gate, and either they hadn't noticed or they didn't care, because they never fixed it. Missy went, *Jesus, fuck!* when we went over the ditch. I reckon her head coulda hit the ceiling. China got out and pushed open the gate. He took a piss standing by the fence.

We parked on the runway, the two cars side by side. Willy got out grinning. He was in the scuzzy trackies he wore to work, and he looked extra lanky.

'You boys been up to much?' he called. Then he looked in the back seat of Foggo's car and saw Missy. 'Fuck's this?'

'Thought we could do something different, eh?' said Foggo.

'I'll smash your fucken face in.'

'What's the matter? You don't want a turn, mate? You wanna sit this one out?'

The car door swung open and Missy fell out onto her knees like a stroke patient. I didn't even see her get up, she was that quick. She just took off sprinting. Her dress was hitched up around her undies. Her hair had come loose. It was flying behind her like a flag. She didn't need to run that fast. Fog would've followed through if she'd stayed there, but he wasn't the sort to chase a girl down, usually. Willy ran after her, then stopped, like he knew he'd never catch her. He yelled her name with his hands cupped round his mouth, then he turned to face Foggo.

'You fucken dog,' he said. His fists rained on Foggo's face before Foggo thumped him in the guts. Willy doubled over. I heard the air go out of him. But he stood up. He and Foggo circled each other. Fog's nose was bloodied, but he looked massive. I'd been thinking Willy was catching up to him. I'd forgotten Fog's mongrel rage. He could swell to twice his own size.

Willy swung wildly, like he'd never been in a fight in his life. He clipped Foggo's jaw. Foggo drew back once. He smashed Willy in the side of the face, and that was it. Willy went down. He put his hands over his ears and lay there. Fog was kicking him in the ribs, in the guts. Finally China and me got it together enough to pull him away. Fog said, *Get the fuck off me*. He stood over Willy. He picked him right up by the shoulders, headbutted him. Willy fell to the bitumen again. Then he and China got in his dead dad's car and drove off.

Willy was face down. He turned his head a bit. His spit was gluey. I counted six teeth sprayed on the ground.

'Can you turn off the lights?' he said at last. His mouth didn't move right. There was blood coming from his ear and his eyebrow was split. I went to his car, switched off the headlights. Nicky was sitting by the driver's side, elbows on his knees. I chucked him the key.

I lay down beside Willy. The asphalt was holding the heat of the day. We were close to the fence, near the only section crowned with barbed wire. There was a shredded plastic bag caught there, flapping. 'Where do you reckon she went,' Willy kept saying, but real quiet.

I don't remember who drove home. Probably me. I don't remember what Willy's parents said about his fucked-up face, one eye swollen shut, or the next time I saw Foggo. We all came apart after that.

The story is Missy went and hid in one of the drains. She was there for two days. No one had any idea where she'd gone. I dunno what Willy told his parents. On the Sunday night there was a bad storm, first real rain in almost a year. The drains flooded and she nearly drowned. Some old bloke found her by chance when he was out looking for his dog and drove her to the base hospital. Later she said she'd wanted to run away because she'd had a fight with her mum. That's what I heard, anyway. Willy's family moved not long after that. Someone said Wodonga, someone else said over the river, far as Griffith. Must have been a fair distance, because I've never run into him playing footy for anyone in the Mid Murray League since.

Nicky got done for arson around that time and went to juvie. He disappeared for ages, and when he came back he was a chippie with a wife and three kids. I see him round sometimes. He's quieter these days, Nicky, and you never see him without his family. His missus got him going to church. Once in a while we'll have a beer together.

China moved to the city after Year Eleven. None of us knows what happened to him. I used to say *Good day* to Mr T whenever I saw him until he died last year, but I never asked about China. I had a weird feeling they stopped talking.

Foggo had some rough years. I think it fucked him up when his dad died. But he came good. Last I heard he was a senior constable working at the Swan Hill station.

These days I'm with Naomi. There are times she won't open up for me, and I know it makes her feel bad. I say, *It's okay, baby*.

FEATURED POET

Michael Ray lives in West Cork. His poems have appeared
in *The Moth*, *The Shop*, *The Penny Dreadful*, *One*, *Southword*,
Magma, *Numero Cinq* and *New Contrast*. In 2012 he was a
winner in the Fish International poetry competition. In
2013 he was shortlisted for a Hennessy Award.

Freedom planet

I'm sure the poster girl moved, as someone
would when working on an all-over tan in, say,
Lanzarote, so that on her return to the Debt
Restructuring Centre, her co-workers
would face a week-long glow with unprompted
anecdotes of all-nighters and cheap alcohol.

The travel agent only moves her mouse,
pretends she isn't watching while I weigh
a week of freedom with my card.

Walking home, I see an up-turned hedgehog
by the kerb, its black eyes collecting gold
rings from the sun. There's human in the pink
toes, and the spines around the snout are flattened
back as if still on a sonic quest to save the world.

Bleak

Now I remember what I might have had—
the chain swinging in a rising tide,
the settling of your anchor in my blood.

Starlings scratching on the roof, sensing light,
frogs returned to the chemistry of pond.
Now I remember what I might have had.

The gutter ticking to a sunrise world;
an afternoon afloat embraced in weed,
the settling of your anchor in my blood.

The rhythmic tug, a lapping sound on wood
turning me to face where we had been.
Now I remember what I might have had.

A shoal of bleak, us watching from the shade,
zigzagging in its ancient family mind;
the settling of your anchor in my blood.

Bare feet, us running on a rippled strand,
rain falling in a bed of just-sewn seed.
Now I remember what I might have had—
the settling of your anchor in my blood.

What have I lived?

I have lived for years
in a small white house
beside the ocean.

I have lived amongst farmers
who dye their fields
and talk precipitation.

I have lived with a woman
who writes to herself
in a room of words,

words that move side-
ways like the nictitating
membranes of birds.

Sometimes she utters phrases
like atmospheric optics,
and I know there'll be rain.

I don't mind the words
my finger can trace in salt
on our table, but I'm still

troubled by the strange
locutions of light
found in the feathers

of boat-tailed grackles,
and how caterpillars
come to have wings.

I have lived with change
as long as I've lived
with the same sun lifting,

each morning, a dark
cloth from a cage
of rearranged continents.

I want

I want to know you—a tongue
dancing in a smoky room.

I want to taste you as a fruit,
cut and weeping.

I want to meet you underwater,
with your weird heat and gentle lament.

I want to fill each gap
between your toes,

I want to wrap you in blue silk—
a flower in the bough of a tree.

I want to watch you undress,
orchestrate deaths.

I want to see you like a glass question—
always from a different angle.

I want to know you
as a myth without the writing.

I want to feel you as the letter O,
between my lips as it's hatching,

I want to hear you
as the sea at dawn,

I want to know you before
you're found and opened

with a careful knife
to find the cause was sorrow.

The gift of water

You know how it is when the room
goes quiet for the one
who'll always be heard and you
pretend to listen, but really
you're humming a stream
in your head, watching the wood-
grain floor roil like water
that's changed its mind
at the bottom of a weir, but is caught
in its own froth. And you think
about how, before cascading,
it must have been a smooth thing,
carrying cloud and impressionist trees,
and only made sound when it rained.

Some biota

Spring, and sand drifts to where the land
rises on its hilly backbone and the track
from Cow Strand begins or ends.
Stone walls still line the island. A hare
flicks up her ears above an ocean
of fiddle-headed fern. Everything
that grows here leans; thistle heads
and scutch bow over the hoof-ruts;
even the stone gable holds an unlikely
tilt. Swallows visit, re-build beside
the lintel, and woodlice work most nights,
shrinking bit by bit the rotten wall-plate.
The threshold sprouts spotted rockrose;
its yellow flowers colour every summer now.

77 pop facts you didn't know about Gil Courtney

Wendy Erskine

1. Gillespie Stanley John Courtney was born in Belfast on July 26th 1950. Also born on July 26th were Aldous Huxley, Jason Robards and Kevin Spacey.

2. Gil Courtney's mother, Elsie, registered him with her maiden name—Gillespie—as his Christian name. She initially said that this was done in error but in later years admitted that it was intentional.

3. Gil Courtney grew up at 166 Tildarg Street, Cregagh, Belfast. Some of the lyrics to the song 'Partial Aperture' on the first The Palomar album, *Golden Dusk*, are often said to have been inspired by the view from the back bedroom of this house. Visible beyond the rooftops are the Castlereagh Hills.

4. Palomar were known as The Palomar until 1975. Thereafter, they were known as Palomar.

5. The phrase 'taking drugs to make music to take drugs to', later used as the title of a Spaceman 3 album, was reputedly first coined by Gil Courtney during the recording of *Golden Dusk*.

6. The front room of the house at 166 Tildarg Street had a silver disc above the mantelpiece. (Although *Golden Dusk* only reached 21 in the UK charts, European sales ensured its silver status.) Gil recalled on a trip home one time taking it off the wall and playing it. 'And what do you think it was,' he said when interviewed in 1972, 'but an Alma Cogan record dipped in silver paint. The paint just flaked off on my hands.'

7. It is likely that Gil Courtney's father was not Alec Courtney, husband of Elsie, and clerk at James Mackie and Sons, Belfast. Elsie was five months pregnant when they married. She was of the opinion that the father was most probably a merchant seaman, possibly Spanish, whom she met in Dubarry's Bar (now McHughs).

8. 166 Tildarg Street was on the market in 2012. The estate agent's description pointed out that it was in need of some modernisation. Photos showed empty rooms, bare walls and floorboards. Elsie Courtney's furniture and carpets had been removed to a skip some weeks earlier.

9. Gil Courtney's first instrument was the xylophone. At primary school a new teacher who introduced a musical half-hour on a Friday afternoon was surprised to see one of her pupils playing two xylophones at once. The young Gil Courtney said he was able to remember the tune of something he'd heard on the radio.

10. Miss Kathleen Hughes, a P7 teacher and church organist, gave Gil Courtney piano lessons in the school assembly hall. She later said that she had never encountered a child with such exceptional ability and whose sight-reading was so extraordinary. When Kathleen Hughes was unable to attend a funeral service owing to illness the eleven-year-old Gil was able to take her place at the organ.

11. Gil Courtney's girlfriend, Simone Lindstrom, went on to have brief relationships with Neil Young and Terry Melcher, son of Doris Day. Dicky Griffin of Palomar described Simone as a 'high-maintenance kind of chick', while Elsie Courtney said she was 'Simone with the little turnip tits in the polo necks you could spit through.'

12. When Gil Courtney was fifteen he began playing with many of the showbands popular in Northern Ireland at the time. He played in groups including The Buccaneers, The Dakotas, The College Boys and The Emperors. Two or three gigs a week would have been common. Ronnie O'Hanlon, drummer in The Dakotas, recalled how they would travel across the province in the back of a van with the equipment: 'A lot of the roads were bad and you were thrown all over the place. A lot of these places were in the middle of nowhere. The driver'd be thinking where in the name of God are we going down this dirt track and then all of a sudden, out of the dark there would be a dancehall, all lit up.'

13. On one occasion when Gil Courtney was due to have his music lesson with Miss Hughes there were numerous boxes of sports equipment stacked on top of the piano. Pupils reported that they had never heard her shout before.

14. The fourth song from Gil Courtney's solo album, *Volonte Blue*, was played by Stuart Maconie on his programme *The Freak Zone* on 6 Music on Sunday 16th October 2011.

15. In the Oh Yeah Music Centre in Belfast there is a small exhibition of Northern Irish pop memorabilia. There is a photograph of Gil Courtney and other members of The Palomar taken outside Gideon Hall's flat in London. They are dressed in the fashions of the time. To the left there is a photo of David McWilliams and to the right a snap of 60s Belfast psychedelic-blues group Eire Apparent.

16. Gil Courtney was educated at Harding Memorial Primary School and Park Parade Secondary School.

17. Gil Courtney used the Hohner Cembalet, the Hammond organ and the Wurlitzer electric piano.

18. Before its eventual closure in 1969, Gil Courtney and other members of both The Dakotas and The Emperors played Hamburg's Star Club. They were part of a group of musicians who briefly went to Germany to 'try their luck'; it was the first time that most of them had been outside Northern Ireland. Gil sent numerous postcards home and Elsie Courtney said that from the spelling and the grammar it was obvious this was a young man who had not spent long enough in school.

19. In *Uncut* magazine's April 2016 feature, 'The Quest for Rock's Great Lost Albums on Vinyl', Gil Courtney's album *Volonte Blue* was listed at number 13. At number 12 was Linda Perhacs' *Parallelograms*.

20. Alec Courtney, Elsie's husband, always used the name Stanley when referring to Gil.

21. In 1968 Gil Courtney moved to London to work as a session musician,

supplementing his wages by joining the house bands at the Dorchester and Park Lane Hotels. 'I never regretted any of my time spent playing in the *palais* bands,' Gil was quoted as having said. 'Many of those guys could really play and I learnt a lot.' During the time that Gil played at the Dorchester, Elsie Courtney and her sister Nan came to London. They stayed in a Dorchester suite, which Gil's connection in reception had managed to secure them *gratis*. 'It was all fine,' Elsie remembered, 'just as long as we always went in the back entrance and up the service stairs and didn't come down for the breakfast.' The sisters danced in the grand ballroom when Gil was playing. 'It was lovely,' Elsie said. 'All the crystal lights. There was a conductor. You should've seen the way the women were dressed. They were beautiful.'

22. The first twenty seconds of the song 'Under the Mountain' from *Golden Dusk* was used as the title music for an Argentinian football programme for five years in the 1980s. Gil Courtney had a co-writing credit on this and therefore received royalties, along with those for his contribution to several other songs on the record.

23. For a period of time 166 Tildarg Street was a popular destination for those bands who were playing Belfast and did not want to stay in a hotel. Elsie Courtney had fond memories of some of the people who stayed with her. Her favourite was Steve who could still sing the songs from *Oliver!*, the West End show in which he performed as a child. She said that he gave a rendition of 'Consider Yourself' in the kitchen, singing the final chorus up on the table.

24. Steve Marriott's band, The Small Faces, borrowed Gil Courtney's electric piano when they played the Floral Hall in Belfast. Ian McLagan's piano was not playing properly. The Floral Hall, an art deco ballroom overlooking Belfast, is now in disrepair and is used to store animal feed for the nearby zoo.

25. Gil Courtney was 6 feet 1 inch tall. His shoe size was 10.

26. Gideon Hall from Palomar published his autobiography in 2005. It was translated into nine languages.

27. Gil Courtney's work as a session musician brought him into contact with a drummer Kevin Heyward who had recently joined a band with two guitarists

he had met through a mutual friend. Kevin Heyward invited Gil Courtney along to rehearse. This was the birth of The Palomar.

28. Gil Courtney rarely wore any colour other than black.

29. Alec Courtney did not approve of rock and roll, Gil's career or the guests who sometimes arrived at Tildarg Street. Elsie remembered him as an 'old stick in the mud who was happier down at the bible study.'

30. Gideon Hall was rather scathing about Elsie Courtney whom Gil would occasionally bring over for shows in London and Glasgow. 'God spare us all from the living embodiment of the oral tradition,' he was quoted as saying. 'What are the words guaranteed to strike most dread in me? *The motherfucking mother's here.*'

31. During breaks in session work, Gil Courtney would read paperbacks, usually either Agatha Christie or American sci-fi stories. 'Simone tried to get me into poetry, Ginsberg and so on, but I never really dug it.'

32. In his autobiography, Gideon Hall said of Courtney, 'I daresay it sounds harsh, perhaps it is, but really, was he anything more than a footnote? If even that? The myth of the beautiful loser. It's tired. It's tiresome.'

33. Gil Courtney went on a trip to Marrakech with a group of friends including Brian Jones of The Rolling Stones, shortly before the latter's death. Popular amongst the crowd was the local *kif*. Elsie couldn't remember whether Brian Jones had ever come to Tildarg Street. 'All these fellas, the girls might have had them on their walls but if they seen what I seen in the morning, dirty pants and them stinking of sweat and what have you, they might have thought different.'

34. *Golden Dusk* was described optimistically and ultimately accurately by Charles Shaar Murray as a 'prelude to greatness.' It received generally positive reviews in *Melody Maker* and *New Musical Express*, with critics particularly praising the Gideon Hall / Dicky Griffin-penned 'Goldline' and 'Damascus'. The songs on which Gil Courtney had co-writing credits were noted for their 'somewhat baroque excess.'

35. 'Goldline' was released as a single. It got to number 34 in the British charts but fared rather better in France. The band had a promo slot on a French television programme in 1972, the first one minute and twenty-three seconds of which can be viewed on YouTube. Gil Courtney for most of this time is just out of shot.

36. When Gideon Hall's autobiography was published it was selected by Eason's for inclusion on their roster for priority in-store promotion. Elsie Courtney was reprimanded by a member of Eason's staff in Donegall Place, Belfast, for moving some of the Gideon Hall books off the prominent display.

37. In January 1973 there was a drugs bust at Gil Courtney's Pimlico flat where a party was in progress. The raid allegedly discovered grass, cannabis resin and Mandrax tablets. Owing to Gil Courtney's apparent medical problems, a psychiatrist was able to make the case that he should receive a suspended sentence. It meant, however, that Courtney was unable to obtain a visa to tour overseas.

38. In a Q&A in *Pop Starz* magazine in the same year Gil Courtney answered the following: Favourite food? Ice cream and jelly. Favourite drink: tea. Favourite colour: yellow. Favourite way to spend a day: going for a walk in the park with friends. Favourite type of girl: nice.

39. In a 1993 interview, Van Morrison was asked if he could remember Gil Courtney. He said no.

40. Gil Courtney had a phobia of flying which he tried to alleviate through alcohol and drug use. Even a short flight would induce a panic attack. On a flight to France in 1972 he was unconscious when the group landed at Charles de Gaulle airport. He made the return journey by land and sea, arriving in London approximately two weeks later. Elsie Courtney said that she could never understand Gil's fear of airplanes. 'Well I don't know,' she said. 'What in the name of God's the problem? How could you not like it? I love getting on a plane. I love the drinks and the food in the little compartments and I love the air-hostesses and I love the duty-free.'

41. Gil Courtney failed to turn up for two concerts, one at Glasgow Barrowlands and the other at Manchester Free Trade Hall. The Palomar's manager at the

time, Lenny Enlander, was dispatched to the Pimlico flat to tell Gil that he no longer had a place in the group. Enlander said later that 'It was hard to tell if Gil was actually there. Some guy I'd never seen before opened the door. It was like a *tabagie*. Smoke-filled. With blackout curtains on every window. I didn't want to tell him with other people there but Gil didn't want to leave and they didn't want to leave. I just said that's it, Gil. You can't go on. He didn't seem all that bothered. But then I didn't know if he entirely understood what I was saying, if you know what I'm saying.' Lenny Enlander did not stay in music management. He ended up running a successful imports-exports business off the Great Eastern Road.

42. The web-based T-shirt business Avalanche Tees printed a limited run of T-shirts bearing the front cover of *Volonte Blue* after the feature in *Uncut*. These were available on Amazon and eBay later, at a reduced price. One of the T-shirts was sent to Texas.

43. Studio musicians who worked on *Volonte Blue* were unanimous in declaring the process tortuous. Courtney expected them to work up to twenty hours a day yet there were also periods when he would disappear for hours at a time and they would be left to their own devices. 'After the, what, fiftieth take, I was finished,' bass player Mac McLean said. 'I have worked with some picky bastards but the man was just insane. Charming for sure, but insane. "Play this like a peach being placed on a terracotta tile. In Marrakech." You know? Impossible.'

44. Gil Courtney and Simone Lindstrom were described in one magazine at the time as 'the most photogenic couple in London.' The magazine featured a photo of the pair in a sitting room with an ornately corniced high ceiling; Simone was in a filmy white dress and reclining on a sofa smoking a cigarette while Gil was crouched in front of her in a black suit. The picture could be regarded as a chilly version of Dylan's *Bringing It All Back Home* cover. The accompanying article profiled the couple in some detail and stated that Gil Courtney's imminent solo album was eagerly awaited.

45. The artwork for *Volonte Blue* features a striking image of an animal (non-specific) lying dead in the middle of a blue desert. Responsible for the cover was Peter Christopherson of the design group Hipgnosis and later of the band Throbbing Gristle.

46. The song 'Tint', the lead track on Side 2 of *Volonte Blue* was said by Gil to have been inspired by cellophane sweet wrappers.

47. When Alec Courtney died of a heart attack in 1975, Gil Courtney was unable to return home for the funeral.

48. The reception *Volonte Blue* received was lukewarm. Some critics praised the '*naif* charm' of some of its lyrics and others its 'loosening of formal structures' but for many listeners it was characterised by incoherence and indulgence. Gil's health-related issues meant that the tour to promote the album had to be postponed, and then eventually cancelled.

49. The Palomar's second album, *CCS*, regularly makes it on to lists of the top 50 albums ever recorded. Gil Courtney, interviewed in *Melody Maker* in 1975, was asked if he had listened to *CCS*. After a pause he said, 'Yes, I have.' And then he was asked if he thought it was as good as everyone seemed to think it was. Gil took a long drag on his cigarette. And then he slowly exhaled. 'Yes,' he said. 'It's that good. What else can I say?'

50. In 1978 Gil Courtney played two shows with The Only Ones.

51. Gil Courtney returned to Belfast in 1980. It was no longer viable for him to remain in London. He travelled to Stranraer by train and got the ferry to Larne. Elsie Courtney met him at the station at York Road and was alarmed for several reasons. 'Well, first thing,' she said, 'he had no suitcase with him or anything like that, just a plastic bag with a few things in it.' She was also shocked by his skeletal appearance because at that point in his life he was eight and a half stone.

52. A three-second sample from 'Choler', the third song on Side 1 of *Volonte Blue* was used as a loop by the Dutch DJ Lars van Tellingen in 2001.

53. When Gil was a child, he and Elsie regularly used to visit the waterworks in North Belfast and feed the swans.

54. Gil Courtney had various food obsessions. Elsie Courtney stated that when he returned to Belfast he only wanted to eat food that was white. After a diet for

some months of only potatoes, pasta and rice he then decided he only wanted to eat food that wasn't white.

55. In 1989 a student film society at the University of Leeds was making a vox-pop programme to be shown on student network television. The production team stopped random people in the street to ask them what music was important to them and why. The fifth person they filmed on a morning in April was a man, mid-thirties, balding, in a grey jacket. 'The music that means most to me,' he said, 'well, okay, the music that means most to me is without a doubt the music of Gil Courtney who played with The Palomar. His music is for me just, just transporting.' He paused but the camera was still pointed at him so he continued. 'It just, what it does is, it just—penetrates to the heart of what it means to be lonely, or in love or to feel a failure and so, and so, at times I've found great comfort in his music, well, *Volonte Blue* is what I'm talking about really, not so much any of the other stuff he was involved with at all really, but other times you know I've found it exhilarating and a total affirmation of what it is to be alive. And I am not really overstating that, like, I do feel that. There's warmth there and there's strangeness there.' He paused again. 'That enough?' The man, embarrassed, laughed, blinked his eyes and put down his head. 'Okay, I think that probably is enough.'

56. For Christmas each year Elsie bought Gil a black merino wool crew-neck sweater.

57. When living again in Tildarg Street, Gil Courtney had a gramophone player and a few records that he played on very low volume. Elsie Courtney said that when you went into the room you wouldn't even have known anything was playing, if you hadn't seen the record rotating.

58. Elsie said that Gil never watched the television. He would only listen to the radio.

59. Gil Courtney used a EMS Putney VCS 3, generally regarded as the first portable analogue synthesiser.

60. A group of teenage girls were interviewed in 1971 for a German magazine's piece on the London music scene. Viv Vallely, 17, said, 'Of all the guys in all the

bands the one I like the most is Gil Courtney from The Palomar. He's not like the singer or anything, he just plays the piano thing, but he's so handsome. And I love the way he speaks cos it's Irish and my granny is Irish. He spoke to me and my friends once when we was waiting outside.'

61. For fifty years the 'house next door', 168 Tildarg Street, was occupied by Arthur McCourt, who was quoted as saying, 'There is something to be said, I really do believe, for being ordinary and having no great talent at anything. I would really wonder if it would have been better for that fella to have gone into a job just like his father, gone to work at Mackie's or wherever, got married, had a couple of kids than go like a firework then nothing. In fact worse than nothing cos I saw the state of him. And for what? What's he got to show, some tunes nobody listens to?'

62. Late one evening in November 1990, as Gil was making his way to the Co-op on the Cregagh Road for cigarettes, he was the victim of robbery and assault. His wallet was stolen and he sustained a broken jaw and a four-inch cut to the side of his head.

63. From 1981 to 1996 Gil Courtney had a repeat prescription for opiate analgesics. Elsie Courtney, who was a patient at another GP practice, supplemented this with a supply of Tramadol, obtained despite her own very good health.

64. Gil Courtney was an aficionado of a magazine entitled *Seven Wonders of the Ancient World* that came out in 1994. Each monthly issue included a scale model of a particular construction. Issues one and two were The Great Pyramid of Giza and the Temple of Artemis at Ephesus. By issue three, however, few newsagents stocked the title, and Elsie Courtney visited numerous shops around Belfast to find that month's issue. The Lighthouse of Alexandria, issue 4, was found in the newsagent in Queen's Arcade, minus the model component.

65. Old bandmate Gideon Hall appeared on the Sunday Times Rich List in 2010, but did not feature in subsequent years owing to poor property investments.

66. Neighbour Arthur McCourt said that when Gil Courtney died all the life went out of Elsie. 'That was it for her. She'd lived for the fella. There wasn't a lot of point for her after that.'

67. Gil Courtney never learned to drive.

68. The vox-pop filmed by the students from Leeds University, where a passer-by talked about Gil Courtney, did not make it to the final programme because a passing bus rendered the sound too poor in quality.

69. In the later years of his life, Gil Courtney would get up at dawn and walk to the centre of the town. When the buses bringing in students, schoolchildren and workers arrived at City Hall he would walk back home again.

70. The instruments on *Volonte Blue* were the following: harmonica, bass, violin, oboe, guitar, drums, organ, keyboards, synthesiser and mandolin.

71. In Gil Courtney's room he always wanted a bare light bulb. 'I would say to him there's nice lampshades in the town,' Elsie said, 'but he said no, he liked staring up at the filament. He liked the way it glowed.' She added, 'I'd rather have the place half decent but Gil was Gil.'

72. The first record Gil Courtney ever bought was 'Battle of New Orleans' by Lonnie Donegan.

73. When Gil Courtney received his diagnosis he opted not to receive any treatment, since chemotherapy would prolong life by only a few months. In the final days when Elsie could no longer look after him, he was moved to the hospice on the Somerton Road. On his windowsill at the place there was an amaryllis, just coming into bloom, Elsie remembered.

74. A journalist who interviewed The Palomar just after the release of *Golden Dusk* said, 'Tensions were pretty palpable. Gil was funny and intense and very likeable, but he was unpredictable and in some ways utterly clueless. They—Gideon and Dicky—they were very assured, public school background, with all that entails. Kevin was just the drummer. Gil was hardly the boy from the back streets but he was a destabilising element that they wanted to jettison. And Gil made it easy for them with the way he behaved. Gideon and Dicky, they might have the counter-cultural credentials, but on another day, with another roll of the dice, they could well have ended up in charge of ICI or BP. They were those

sorts of people. The juggernaut that Palomar became would tend to bear that out.'

75. Gil Courtney's funeral took place in the Chapel of Rest on the Ravenhill Road. It was attended by only a handful of people, including a former member of The Dakotas and one of The Emperors. Elsie Courtney, in the belief that there would be a record player, had brought a battered and scratched copy of *Volonte Blue* but there was only a CD player available. Ronnie O'Hanlon had a couple of compilation CDs in his car, one of which was *Feelin' Good Vol. 1*, free with the *Daily Mail*. A decision on a track was quickly made. As they filed out of the chapel, 'Everybody's Talkin'' by Harry Nilsson was played, the music from *Midnight Cowboy*.

76. Gillespie Stanley John Courtney died in Belfast on February 2nd 2001. Fred Perry, Gene Kelly and Bertrand Russell also died on February 2nd.

77. Gil Courtney's favourite cigarettes were Chesterfields.

Absolutely Bloody Final

I read him letters discovered in a wardrobe.
Caress a dromedary of blue neck bones.
Old memories erupt, like unruly rhododendrons.

My feet step gingerly around incessant TV noise.
He turns the volume louder, until it drowns out fear.
Each swallow takes three minutes to go down. *Let's talk*

about something else. Outside, the sky's a heated
dome. He's asking me to pray for rain,
for my non-believing children. He says

my mother's still as present as the light flickering
across the water. Dragonflies spike the surface,
spooking other insects. He watches from her bed,

which he refuses to abandon, although it's old
and saggy. Our family converges, as untuned
as his piano, long past early joys.

A raven and a crow settle on each shoulder.
He tells me faith is so much more beautiful
than a body breaking down, all the way to bone

and organ. Flings the sheet aside. I flap my hand
until he's covered. The children laugh,
call him a nudist. Through the French doors,

he observes the coming purple, their swallow dives.
Clouds spill for seven minutes, lash the swimming pool.
When electricity returns, I make a pot of tea.

Still, we're skirting. On the TV: *I'll get back to you.*
An old soldier's final order: *I'd like an ABF.*
The children go out, get Absolut.

Afric McGlinchey

Note: In our family an ABF is an 'absolutely bloody final' drink which visitors are
required to declare before my father will let them leave the house. Absolut is the
name of his favourite vodka.

SPAR at 3.30pm

There'll be hard rain coming,
thick, quick walls of it within the hour.
There's a swell ready to drop with water
that's been waiting for weeks, and it will be hard.
We've just had it too good this summer, the dad says

as we stop off at the red corner shop because milk needs to be got.
These days it's a barber's and a bar and lounge as well as the shop.
I've got enough of a hairstyle as it is, and if I go in for one now
my dad will have four and we can't be half-cut for dinner,
so just the milk it is. Out I hop and across the way

there's another bar that doubles as a funeral home,
the black and white paint doing the job
for a place where you'd get a pint plus a prayer,
no travel required for your troubles, we've it all built in.
Two birds, one stone, *tomb*stones,
I could go on but people are there right now, sweating out bullets

through eased up dotted ties and undarkened black suits,
leaning on the windows, dragging the Lord
baby Jesus and all the saints out of a pack
of Silk Cut Blue arguing how people are related to the dead.

I go in and get the milk with the very best date
and join the queue of three and there's a man
in front of me in blue jeans battered near seamless
and real black shoes gripping the life out of a bottle of
Blossom Hill that's slipping away from him altogether,
his hand shaking not with nerves or excitement
but with one of two possible problems. He grunts, he pays in pennies,
he leaves, and smiles wide walking out the door.

I didn't notice until I got back outside that the sky had given up waiting
and the rain had been let loose, direct and down, straight, solid, strong,
but the mourners were still stood outside, finishing their fags, staring across,
straight, solid, strong, determined to drag it out to the very last.

Paul McCarrick

Visual Purple

Force an albino rabbit
to stare at black and white
chequered patterns or
portraits of Salvador Dalí
Behead it and remove
an eye under sodium light

Find a man who drowned
his sons shortly following
the death of his wife
Ensure he faces the guillotine
and wait with chemicals
and a basket for his head

Look up to the stars and
tell someone you want to
sleep with how the light
seen is long extinguished
How you're staring backwards
into an ocean of time

Write down in your little
notebook how you glimpse
violent movements
in the dead man's retina
Remember his head was
sack-covered at the end

Dylan Brennan

Trouble

Philip Ó Ceallaigh

Engine roaring, I rode the bike hard into the sun, towards the bay, jolting across uneven stubbled earth, wind in my face. The summer was focused and peaked in this pure vision; fields beneath enormous sky, a brimming glassy bay, the sand dunes lying like a jagged mountain chain along the horizon.

I was seventeen years old.

I turned tight, almost losing the wheels from under me, tasted my own exhaust smoke, then came upright again, bike in too high a gear, shuddering till it caught speed, and aimed for the open gate to the upper field. The ruts from tractor wheels were parched canyons in the gateway. Rocks poked through the gouged dusty earth. I needed to slow for it. I accelerated.

Passing through the gateway, the world shook me loose.

And then I was staring at the blue empty sky.

I lay there in perfect silence and stillness. I was completely aware of where I was, and all that had happened in the days and weeks preceding that moment. I was aware of my life and my troubles. But my troubles no longer belonged to me. They were clamouring little objects I watched from above, blessedly free of them, just as I observed the desperation of my body as my throat made foul funny noises, begging for breath. I had heard of the soul, of course—I had kneeled in the gloom of the church—but now I could feel it, knocked loose there inside my ribcage, ready to detach itself and rise and dissolve itself in the blue. And I wondered if my back was broken.

I heard a groan as the breath entered me, and I panicked, feeling the body clutching at me again, pulling me down. The blue was gone, because my eyes were squeezed shut. Now the thought that my back was broken was horror. It was the fear of the flesh, pinned to the earth. I had to move. Someone slapped my leg. My head jerked up and my eyes opened. I was alone.

The motorcycle was on its side, a wheel still spinning.

I sat up and watched it.

I had left my body and returned to it. It had happened between two breaths.

I sat there in the dust. The wheel slowed and stopped.

Time was not what I had previously believed it to be. I had just stepped out of it.

I got up, looking around, glad my legs worked. I was still slightly deaf. I was still inhabiting the vision, and wanted to hold on to it a little longer, but breath by breath, I could feel it slipping away. I looked at the countryside, at the world I was returning to. The bales of straw were arranged in eights, here and there about the field, where I had stooked them. The grain was in the silo, the straw would soon be in the barn. And then we would raze the stubble, trailing burning plastic fertilizer bags across the ground. The bushes and trees and sky would tremble in the heat-haze and drifting smoke as the fire caught and moved in a line across the land.

A couple of weeks before this happened, before I was hurled like a rag doll to the hard earth—and discovered that I was a soul, and that time was just an obsession, a condition, of the body, and that thought itself, compulsive and time-bound, was the fault of the body—I had become a man. She was a couple of years older than me. I was remembering her naked when I accelerated at that wrong moment.

Her family was away that afternoon, and I'd ridden the bike in to town. In the kitchen she gave me beer and offered me a cigarette. I looked at it and shook my head. I'd never smoked. She smoked a lot. I liked that about her. I liked everything about her. I wanted to kiss her. I'd kissed girls before, but never sober.

—Say something, Space.

They called me Space. It had been Spaceman once. I moved under another gravity, like a moonwalker.

I shrugged and drank some beer.

I tried hard to think of something to say, but nothing happened. It was like the thing with the chickens; someone had done an experiment, putting food on the other side of their wire. They crowded together, squawking like crazy, looking at the food. It was discovered that really hungry chickens would starve to death even if the gate to the run was left open—they couldn't tear their eyes from the food. Less hungry chickens would go for a stroll and eventually stumble across their dinner. Which drove the starving chickens on the other side mad.

I couldn't relax and talk properly. I wanted too much to kiss her.

—I never know what you're thinking about, she said.

I told her about the chicken experiment. She listened patiently, nodding from time to time, smoking, and said:

—You're great company, Space.

She walked out of the kitchen. I felt ashamed. I looked at her cigarettes on the table. Maybe it was time to try one. I could hear her in the other room. I followed her. She was looking out the window at the back garden, smoking. I stood beside her. I wondered if she wanted me to leave. She extinguished her cigarette and said:

—What do you want to do?

I shrugged and said:

—Drink some beers. Whatever you want to do is fine.

She turned and walked away, down the hall. I watched her go, beautiful and severe, long black hair swaying. She went into a room. I could hear her doing something.

I went back into the kitchen. She'd left her cigarettes on the table. I looked at them. I finished the beer. I took another from the fridge and opened that and took a drink. I brought it with me down the hall, quietly, and looked into the room she'd entered. I couldn't see her. It was dim. The curtains were pulled. I took several small steps into the room. She was in bed, under the covers, looking at me.

—What's wrong? I whispered. Are you sick or something?

—Take your clothes off.

I put my beer on the dresser and took my clothes off and got in beside her.

It was different, kissing someone and our naked bodies touching and hands moving all over. Many things were happening at once. No wonder, I thought, this is so popular.

—Your cock is very big.

—Yeah.

—No, I mean, compared to other men.

I'd never been called a man before. It didn't bother me about all the other cocks she was familiar with. Their owners were away in other places—working in petrol stations and farms and warehouses, or sitting in bars and kitchens—and it was mine she was gripping now.

—Is it a problem?

—We'll soon find out.

—I don't have a condom.

It wasn't strictly necessary, she said. She explained how it worked. It sounded easy. But still, what if...

—You want to do it or not? she demanded

Afterwards, we sat in the kitchen again. She offered me a cigarette. I shook my head. She lit up and smoked.

—Why are you looking at me like that? she asked.

—Can we do it again?

—Right now?

—Sometime.

She laughed

—You're great company, Space.

She finished her cigarette. I finished my third beer.

—Well, you'd better get out of here, or they'll be carrying you out.

Indeed, I seemed to be melting, slumping down into the chair. I did as I was told, getting to my feet. I felt pretty good. Relaxed but light.

She walked me to the front door and opened it. I went out and got on the bike. I didn't have a helmet. But I didn't have tax or insurance either. Or a licence. She was at the edge of town. It was open country through to where I lived.

I rode homewards, sun on my face.

I stood up and looked around. The sky was cloudless. The bay was still brimming, the tide on the point of turning. I was unhurt. I was in no hurry to get back to the world of doing and thinking and feeling. I pulled the bike upright and examined it. It seemed fine. I got on and kick-started it. It turned first time and I rode it gently up to the house.

It was an old house, two storeys, painted white, built in the nineteenth century. There was a giant fireplace in the living room, big enough that you could stand in it. My father had been born in that house. I rode the bike into the courtyard and parked it. There were stables and outhouses, plastered and painted white also. In places the plaster had fallen off, revealing red brick. Nobody was home. And in the silence when the engine died I looked at the house and I understood what was going to happen. I had never envisaged the future before except in the vaguest terms, in daydreams and longings, but now it presented itself as a fact, another aspect of my sudden lucid vision, another thing I would be able to tell no one, except when it had already come to pass: that this house would one day be a ruin. My parents would be gone from it, my brothers and sisters would be gone, the old trees would be cut down, the roof would fall in, a tree would grow from the floorboards in the room where my parents had slept. Everything before me now that was whole would be undone, and I would live to see it.

It was Sunday and it was silent and still because they were away at the moving statues. Statues of the Blessed Virgin had begun to move, to gesture to the faithful. It had started down the coast from us, in Ballinspittle, and now statues in townlands all over the country were moving. The believers would congregate to kneel and pray, day and night, in every weather, staring, awaiting her next sign. News and talk shows brought the latest reports; a group of maidens in Donegal, walking home from an evening of set dancing, had seen a light in the sky above a hedgerow, the face of Our Lady appeared and told them to prepare themselves for the coming message. The land trembled on the brink of revelation.

So I entered the living house that day seeing that it would one day be a ruin, alone with my vision, because the folks were away, expecting bigger news.

I went up to my room. It was dim and ghostly after the brightness of the open country. Through the window I could see the flat-topped Comeraghs out to the west. I wished I was walking on their heights, from where you could see half the world. A slowly growing crack of anxiety had appeared in the perfection of my earlier mood. I sat down on the bed and rubbed my eyes. Then I picked up the book lying open on the bed. I had been reading it that morning but could remember nothing of it. I looked at the page and the lines jumped out at me:

> Just as a reservoir is of little use when the whole
> Countryside is flooded, the illumined man
> Has little need of scriptures, seeing as he does
> Divinity in everything around him.

I heard an engine I recognised and I stood up, dropping the book to the floor.

I went down. Joe was standing in the yard by the bike in his test-fighter pilot pose, helmet under one arm, feet planted apart, long curly hair already springing back. Around his neck he wore a red and white Palestinian headscarf. He was a year older than me.

—Howya, Space. Quiet round here. Isn't it?

—They're away at the statues. Down at Mount Mellory. The Ma says she feels something is going to happen.

He took out his cigarettes, put one in his mouth, and lit a match, looking at me:

—You know? I fucken wish it would.

He leaned into the flame, then looked at me again and said, smoke spilling from his mouth:

—What's the matter with you?

I shook my head. I couldn't tell him anything. It didn't seem possible.

—You look like you've been sniffing solvents.

I shrugged.

—Well. I won't beat about. S'pose you heard already.

—No, I lied.

—G-wan-ya-did.

I said nothing. He took a couple of puffs in short succession, looking at me, maybe trying to figure me out.

—It's like this. It happened and I'm more surprised than anyone. Well. There you have it.

I nodded. He didn't need to say her name. It was there already.

—I wanted to tell you, to your face. Because I know you used to like her.

—I still do like her, Joe.

—Sure why wouldn't you, she's a good one.

—Yeah.

At this point the crows in the trees around got off on one of their panics and I looked up at them and thought something would happen. And Joe looked up but already they were starting to settle and he thought less of it and it was over soon, except for some squawking.

—I know you had a thing for her, so. Out of respect. No hard feelings.

I shook my head.

—Well, Space, you're alright. It's a load off, to talk to you. I suppose you want to know how it happened.

—No.

—We were drinking, the gang of us, down at the sand dunes, and I walked off and lay down and was looking at the sky. I just seemed to wake up and she was on top of me. There I was, looking up at the stars and getting my hole. And drunk as I was, boy, I remembered you were into her. I thought of you. But it was too late anyway.

—Ah, sure.

—It was a good ride. Very natural, finding a young one on top of your knob like that. Pure fucken poetry. The firelight and the stars in the open air and all. But the thing is.

He looked at me meaningfully.

—What is?

—I mean it's not just getting the ride and all. I really like the girl.

—That's good, Joe.

—Yeah, well, we'll see how it goes. You never can tell.

I nodded. Joe dropped what was left of his cigarette and ground it under his boot.

—Well.

—Give us a smoke there.

—Yeah.

He tapped out a Camel and I took it. I put it in my shirt pocket. He didn't comment, though he knew I never smoked.

—You're fucken all right, Space, so you are.

I couldn't argue. It was his film. I was a supporting actor.

—Can I have the matches too?

He handed them over. He put on his helmet and got on and kick-started the bike. It was a powerful machine, unlike mine. I had a big cock, though. Then again, I'd only really used it once and it hadn't brought me luck. We waved goodbye and Joe took off. I watched him go. Then I stood there, listening to him accelerating down the road, ripping the gentle countryside apart with his noise. I wandered over to the chicken run and gripped the wire and stared in at the hens.

It got dark and late and still I was on my own. Something must have been going on at the statues, perhaps the Second Coming, and I was the last soul in the country to hear about it. They were living pages from the Book of Revelation, while I was tormented by images of firelight orgies at the sand dunes, naked bodies leaping and dancing and copulating among the flames. I wandered from silent room to silent room, still with the vision in my mind of the house as a ruin. I opened a cabinet and drank from a bottle of my father's whiskey. He didn't mind me doing that. I don't mind you getting drunk, he told me once, as long as you're not smoking marijuana. People smoked it, he explained, and jumped off buildings, thinking they could fly. I started to feel like the last human being alive on earth. What if they had all ascended on a pillar of light, clutching their rosary beads? I couldn't stay still. There was nothing left of the peace I felt when I came off the bike.

I went out to the yard and paced about in the dark. What I had to do was walk.

I went around the house and through the front gate and down the road, between the dark hedgerows. I emptied the bottle and sent it sailing into the night. It landed with a soft clunk. The stars were out and a sliver of a moon. I walked fast, trying to think of nothing. Then I heard a car engine from very far away. Finally the light from its headlights became visible, then the bright headlights themselves as it rounded a curve and came towards me.

It pulled up beside me. A police car.

The garda at the wheel rolled his window down. There was another guard in the passenger seat and another in the back.

—Howya. Late in the evening to be out for a walk?

—What time is it?

—Late. Where are you going?

—Nowhere.

He frowned. He asked my name and address. I told him.

—Don't believe you. I don't believe you're from round here at all. Who's your neighbours?

I gave them Dalys, Hanleys, Mulcahys and Doyles. Walshes, Powers, Chasteys and Phelans. Meades, Quinlans and Quirkes. I gave them half the county.

—That's enough, you blaggard. Who's your parish priest?

I gripped the car door and leaned towards the cop and told him, loudly, to his face:

—JUST AS THERE IS LITTLE NEED OF A RESERVOIR WHEN THE ENTIRE COUNTRYSIDE IS FLOODED, THE ILLUMINED MAN HAS LITTLE NEED OF PRIESTS, SEEING AS HE DOES THE LORD IN ALL AROUND HIM!

The clicking of three car doors opening together, a rumble of bogman curses, and I was already leaping the iron gate into the field behind me. I sprinted into the darkness, tripping and falling and rolling and laughing and getting up again and running again. I heard sheep bleating somewhere and the pounding of all the little hoofs and it sounded so funny I found it hard to run with the laughter. I could see the shadows of the trees in the hedgerows against the relative brightness of the sky, dusted with stars, and I made for that, knowing the field was bordered with deep drainage trenches. I looked back and could see the torch beams flailing about as the cops hauled themselves over the gate. I slid down the steep side of the drainage trench, coming to a splashing stop in ankle-deep water, boots sinking in weeds and silt on the bottom. The frogs went wild, a chain reaction of frog-hysteria. I held my sides to stop laughing. Snot was hanging out my nose. I looked up at the stars and wanted to howl— the frogs were going jabba-wabba, and the cops were in hot pursuit, shouting hilarious stuff about 'coming in quietly', their thrashing torch beams detonating the branches of the trees above me in joyous flashes—and the sheep weren't bleating any more, they were squealing, having heart attacks, sure their throats would be cut.

I experienced that breakneck urge I'd had that afternoon on the bike, the temptation to call out to the cops to come and get me. I imagined scrambling through the hedgerows and into the next field and taking them cross-country. But I thought better of it. The hedgerow was probably too dense to penetrate. They'd seize me the drainage ditch and we'd splash about like overexcited pigs, their flailing arms making a mudwrestling light show, then they'd haul me out and give me a good kicking.

So I hugged my sides and held in my laughter. Finally the lights stopped flashing about and I heard the clanging of them clambering over the metal gate, muttering to each other. I heard the engine starting, and the car driving away, the noise very clear in the night air, an enormous sound, even as it changed and became distant. I held onto it until I could hear it no more and still I stood there. The frogs were settling down again. It would be as well to stay there with them for a while, and when returning along the road to take shelter at the sound of any vehicle. I was an outlaw now.

It became very quiet. My feet in the water, I gazed up at the unblinking stars. I could feel the cold water, but I was hardly a body anymore. Ever since coming off the motorbike, I hadn't quite settled back into it. I was no longer something solid, I was dissolved in that vast blackness, and I felt my breathing and my heartbeat and the tingling of my skin as a vibration, a faint tremor, just like the trickling of the water in the drainage ditch and the whisper of the leaves in the air above me.

I was crying then. I wonder why my body is crying, I thought, because I feel fine here in the drainage ditch. Those were tears, and my chest was shuddering. But that had happened too when I was laughing, moments before. Shortly, I couldn't tell whether I was laughing or crying. I had been so wound up over the past weeks, wound up in my trouble, and I was exhausted. I had waited so long for my life to begin, and now suddenly this thing with the girl I couldn't understand, and standing in the drainage ditch with the frogs. Observe this helpless shaking of the body, I told myself, wiping the snot and tears with my sleeve.

I patted my pocket. The cigarette was there, and the matches. I took out the cigarette and struck a match and illuminated the little world in front of me, and lit the cigarette. I inhaled. I tossed the match and it hissed. I was in darkness again. I stood in the ditch, the water trickling by my feet, and exhaled, looking upwards to the trembling stars.

Nightstorming

It starts at night when the light goes off. I roll over in the dark and the lid comes off the glass bottle inside me where all the worst thoughts are. They spill across my chest and although I roll back to stop the flow, it's too late.

There's a moment when they're flowing away, before they rebound off the bedroom wall and come back as a wave that carries me out to sea. I toss and turn and tangle in sheets that wrap tight around my legs and drag me lower in the water. I throw off the duvet to lessen the weight on my chest, but I still can't breathe.

All this fighting for the surface, but I when I get there it's to see another wave coming, that's bigger than the last. I'm swimming towards it as fast as I can to get over the top before it breaks. I'm getting higher and higher, and now I'm afraid of falling as well as drowning.

I can't duck through it like surfers do, because it's not really water, it's a memory. It happened the way it happened and when it happened I didn't duck, I fell. But not from here, from higher up. The last feet of the climb are silent and lit by the moon, the wave turns white as it crests and breaks.

Then the falling, the feeling of hundreds of hands squeezing my insides and pulling them just above where they're supposed to be. And if it was in just one place it would be painful enough to wake up, but it's everywhere, and I'm not asleep. I'm not even in bed.

I'm in A&E again, I'm coughing up blood and wondering where it's coming from. I'm passing out in my dad's arms and he's saying 'I've got you' and I'm saying 'I think I'm going to faint' except they're not my words, because what I should be saying is 'I think I'm going to die'.

Except it's a memory, and it happened the way it happened, and I didn't die.

The time flashes out of the dark like a lighthouse's beacon. 02:10… 03:40… 6.00. I'll pass out in the dark of one of the between times. Or later, when the dawn-blue light seeps round the edges of the curtains and the hum of the heating comes on as somebody gets up to go to work. Then I'll know I've made it to the shore again, pull myself up onto the sand and sleep.

Maryanne Doyle

Daisy-Chained Summers

Over long, daisy-chained summers
I wondered

                    how
an imaginary horse might move,

I took on the actions, my hands
were   the   hooves,   my   feet   made   the
noise
and as I galloped, friend after friend
joined me, became a parade.

We wondered

if a lovebird really knew
how to love, or if his feathers
grew like a rainbow,

the truth was all in our eyes

as we rolled ourselves into small
bundles, took on the hills, the grass,
the bark, grazed our bodies,
earned scars for life,

wondered

what adults did all day.

K.S. Moore

The Last Stretch

Eamon Mc Guinness

Before they reached The Yacht, Mick had pissed twice.

'I broke the seal too early, man.'

'Come on to fuck, would you? We'll be on this road all night at this rate.'

Mick's breathing was rough, a wheelie bin full of bottles pulled over cobblestones. The road was dimly lit and the bends were sharp and vicious. Ben knew them instinctively and usually avoided walking this stretch at night.

'He was some bollix, wasn't he?'

'Who?' Ben asked, knowing full well who Mick was talking about.

'That dope of a taxi driver. Who lets two pissed lads out on this road?'

'I'm not pissed.'

'Well, then.'

'You shouldn't have insulted him.'

'Over-sensitive fuck.'

Mick had hardly looked at Ben all night, grunts and side-glances when he wasn't dug into his phone or pointing with his pint at the screen. Ben stopped after three, he was cutting back but hadn't told Mick. He slipped out excuses about a headache and stuff to do in the morning. Mick did all he could to get the night going and after coming from the toilets suggested, hands open and palms up in a sign of peace, they go to the student night in Mulraneys. Ben beat that down quicker than he would a fly. They spent the rest of the night watching the Champions League. They stayed for the interviews and analysis and had one more when the highlights of the early games came on. It was the qualifying rounds and teams they'd never heard of were playing teams they'd only barely heard of.

'These are all shite,' Mick said, looking up from his phone when a goal went in, 'Dundalk could easily mix it with these cunts, look.' He had an article up about one of the teams, the Latvian champions. Their star striker was a baker and after the match would be working through the night to have his shop ready for the morning. He liked it, he said, it gave him time to think about what went right and wrong in the game.

The Yacht had been in and out of different management for years until Mick's uncle Barry bought it a couple of years ago. It looked out of place where it was, as if it had just landed on the crest of the hill at Loughshinny, on the bend between Skerries and Rush. It bordered a farm on its right and a wasteland to its left. Mick worked as a barman there last year, before it closed after Christmas.

'We should've gone to Mulraneys.'

'You could've gone by yourself.'

'Give over, would ya?'

'Never stopped you before.'

While Mick was pissing, Ben walked to the side of the pub. In the empty, chain-locked carpark he climbed onto a worn-out picnic bench. Lambay Island came into view. From this perspective, it looked to Ben like the heart of an animal, ripped from its chest and left on the factory floor to die. He looked at his jeans and runners. He couldn't find his good shoes before he left, so wore his running shoes that had flecks of brown dirt and grass stains on them. His jeans had long since lost their shape. At least he was wearing a shirt, but even in that, combined with his lower half, he looked foolish, half-dressed. Mick sauntered over, kicking a can and smoking. His shoes were brown with a sharp pointed tip, jeans black and neatly pressed, his jacket stylish. He looked healthy, his gym work and physical labour gave him a strong appearance. Ben thought he could be someone famous, a footballer or a pop star. Mick jumped up onto the creaky, weather-beaten bench and the sea came into his field of vision for the first time.

'There she is,' Mick shouted in a voice Ben felt was too loud for the time of night.

'What?'

'All of it, the town, the island, the sea, at least we have this.'

'What?'

'A way out, it's up to us to get out of this kip. Wanna see something?'

'What?'

'C'mon.'

Mick had a naggin in his back pocket. He still went through the motions of their Wednesday night Champions League meetups, when it was clear they were on borrowed time. Nagle had gotten married, Pauly'd had a kid and Jonsey and Frank had fallen out. Ben waved the offer of a drink away. Mick finished it off, threw the bottle into the neighbouring field and turned back to The Yacht. The rear yard was full of empty kegs and bottles stacked in crates. There was a dripping tap, boxes full of posters and bar knick-knacks. The windows had been white-washed but there was a patch big enough for a set of eyes. Ben cupped his eyes like a man blocking out the sun and looked in at the empty bar. Ben thought he heard something and jumped around, but saw nothing. Mick shushed him and undid the back door. There were three locks and he had the keys to all of them.

'What the fuck?'

'Had to open up over Christmas. Barry gave me a pair.'

'Is this where you've been bringing her?'

'Don't you know it, pal, not a fuckin' word to anyone.'

Ben felt that walking through the abandoned pub was like being in someone's bedroom. It felt oddly intrusive, as if you could be caught at any minute. The room had been used for sessions; cans and cigarette butts littered the tables. Ben followed Mick into the lounge, up the back stairs and into the staff-only area.

'Wakey wakey,' Mick called.

'Who are you talking to?'

'You'll see.'

'There's someone here?'

'C'mon.'

'What the fuck, man?'

There was another locked door and Mick opened it. Inside was a single bed.

'This is where we go, but we have to keep the door open.'

'Why?'

'To keep sketch.'

They all knew he'd been shagging Katie, and everyone presumed it was in his car. Ben felt the pressure to say something, to match Mick's high excited voice. It hurt him to think of her here. He swallowed and looked away from Mick. 'Why are we here?' Mick turned and stared at Ben. He bit his lower lip with his upper teeth.

'Why did you ask that?'

'I don't know. But answer me.'

'To do something, I don't know, to go somewhere. We do fuck all anymore.'

Ben walked into the function room that faced the main road. He'd been to twenty-first birthday parties here. The moon was bright and Ben appeared illuminated in the glass of the long bay window. The room was empty except for a ragged couch.

'Don't stand in the light,' Mick said as he pushed him to the side. They both looked out onto the road from behind the protection of the curtains.

'It's not an action movie, man.'

'What?'

'No one's gonna shoot up at the window.'

'I know, I just wouldn't want to be caught here is all.'

'Who'd be around here at this time?'

'You never know.'

There was nothing to do and a wound had spread itself between them. Ben had resisted talking about Katie the whole night.

'Why do you bring her here?'

'I knew that's what you're pissed off about. What's the difference? Here or anywhere else.'

'Well, you're right then, you're right, there's no difference, but an abandoned pub?'

'I know ya introduced us, man, but you can't get between couples.'

'We were good friends though, close, before you got with her, she won't even talk to me now, not properly anyway.'

'What does that mean?'

'We used to talk, you know, coffee and stuff.'

'She was there with us last Friday.'

'Yeah, but I feel strange ringing her now to chat.'

'Why, 'cause I'm with her?'

'Yeah, exactly.'

'Well don't be. I'm just shagging her, man, we're not gonna get married or anything. You coulda gone for it ages ago but you bottled it.'

Two weeks earlier Mick had sent around a picture on the lads' WhatAapp group of him and Katie with the caption #morninblowie attached to it. Ben waited for a few days then deleted WhatsApp, pretending to the lads that there was a glitch on his phone. He hadn't mentioned anything to Mick about it and neither had Mick.

The night was murky black and clouds moved to cover their view of Lambay.

Ben turned away and walked out of the room. As he did so, he heard coughing above him.

'What the fuck is that?'

'Another surprise for you, Benny. C'mon we see if this cunt's awake.'

'Who?'

'Bojan.'

'Who?'

'Bojan Bojan, how many fuckin' Bojans do you know?'

'None.'

The coughing was followed by shuffling and Ben was reminded of mice running through floorboards as a child. It sounded like someone trying to make their way through a dark, cluttered space. Ben zipped up his jacket, making ready to leave.

'Who the fuck is up there, Mick?'

'Calm down, man. I just told ya. Polish Bojan from the glasshouses. Works for Finnegan. You know him, he was the cellar-man here over Christmas.'

'I thought his name was Pavel?'

'That's just what we called him when we couldn't remember his real name.'

'What's going on, man?'

'This is what I've wanted to tell you. Barry left me the keys when he went to Oz, told me to keep an eye on the place. Rats, rising damp, that sort of stuff. He throws me a few quid. So I starts bringing Katie here. Barry turned a couple of the offices into bedrooms so at night we'd meet at the corner and sneak in, couldn't be seen parking or anything like that. So we're here one night and who do I find in a sleeping bag out beside the kegs, a little fuckin' roof made out of boxes and crates but our man Bojan. I wake him up and guess what he's got in his sleeping bag?'

'What?'

'A fuckin' hammer. It takes him a minute to remember who I am, he's all dozy and shit and mixing up his languages but we bring him into the pub and he tells us how his missus has kicked him out. So I gets a brainwave. I ask him if he wants to move in while my uncle's away. It was fairly cold out you know? He agrees and we bring him to the upstairs office, there's a jacks up there, he has access to the kitchen and he's still working during the day. He sneaks out in the morning, locks up and keeps an eye on the place at night.'

'And what?'

'What? Oh yeah, he pays me seventy quid a week and keeps his mouth shut about me and Katie.'

'He hasn't been with her, has he?'

'No to fuck, of course not, wouldn't let that pig near her, smell of fuckin cabbage off him. He stays upstairs when he knows I'm coming. I always text him first. C'mon, let's go say hello. He's expecting us.'

They walked up a little flight of stairs. Mick knocked three times, shouted 'wakey wakey, hands off snakey,' and opened the door slowly. Ben stared at Bojan. He was in his sleeping bag, covered with a duvet and propped up by a cushion and two pillows. The only light was a desk lamp stretched from the wall and nestled on a crate. Bojan's hands were directly under the light and he was rolling a collection of cigarettes. Ben scanned the room slowly. A makeshift clothesline hung from one corner to the other and five damp shirts were pinned on it. Work boots were resting on another upturned crate in the corner and a Man United kids schoolbag sat on a chair. On the desk was a chess board, ready to be played. The round stained-glass window just below the roof was cracked where someone threw a stone through it after the pub closed.

'Is that you, Bojan?'

'Of course it is me, who else?'

'I thought it might have been the Latvian baker.'

Mick winks at Ben and he smiles back, in spite of himself.

'I'm Polish. You know this.'

'I'm only messing. Were your team playing tonight?'

'No, we are in the later games.'

'La-de-da. Will I throw a bit of green into that?'

'Ok, take this one, I start another.'

'Bojan spends half the night rolling smokies,' Mick says to Ben.

'It helps when I can't sleep.'

Ben didn't know that Mick was back smoking weed. They'd quit together in January. A life he didn't know cut him and Ben felt all these small betrayals stick to him. He encouraged distance in people, he knew that. He stood up while the lads chatted about football and peeked his head behind Bojan's clothes. On tippy toes, he looked through the hole in the glass down to the road. He tried to remember his view of the window from below, but couldn't picture it now without seeing his shadow behind the broken glass. He wanted a rich, secret life like Mick had and was thinking of this when he heard Katie's name.

'Katie, you don't see her tonight?'

'No, I was out with this stale prick instead.'

Bojan looked at Ben fully for the first time and broke into a wide, chipped-tooth smile.

'I remember him. Quiet one. What is your drink again? Something strange.'

'Smithwicks with a Guinness head.'

'First time I hear this.'

'Picked that up in college. Always has to be different this cunt, he was the same in school.'

'You friends from school?'

'Yeah, but he's a college boy now.'

'What you study?'

'Business, but I'm not going back.'

'Yeah? You never told me that?'

'Telling ya now.'

'So Katie come or no?'

'I'm gonna text her now, see if I can make something of the night.'

'Now?'

Ben's voice sounded high in his head, screechy and out of control, but his question was ignored and he wondered if he'd said anything at all.

'You bring her back?'

'No, her ma's car is parked 'round the corner from the gaff. I'll meet her there. Don't worry, man, you can wank in peace.'

'Wank in peace. Funny guy.'

Ben walked the last stretch in near silence. All he could see was a toasted sandwich, a cup of tea and his bed. Mick's speech was slurry and unpredictable. The night had turned cold and Ben felt underdressed. They were at the turn for Katie's estate and he was rubbing his hands to keep warm. Mick stopped to piss again and Ben looked back up the hill. He felt the distance closing in between the town and The Yacht, as if they were walking on stepping stones over a river.

'You know we could do what we like to him, don't you?'

Ben's eyes travelled to Mick's, but they didn't connect.

'What does that mean?'

'I mean, he's ours, you know? We could make him dance. No one would know or care, would they?'

'What are you talking about, man?'

'Bojan.'

'He seems okay.'

'Yeah, but I'm just saying the possibilities.'

'There are no possibilities.'

'I heard he was kicked out for hitting his wife around.'

'Where did you hear that?'

'The auld lad told me. We owe that cunt nothing. If we wanted to we could take advantage of the situation.'

'Where does he wash his clothes?'

'The sink in the kitchen. Fuckin' smell of the place. Just think about it.'

'How long are you gonna keep it going?'

'I haven't decided yet but I need to use him more, take advantage. It makes me feel better having him there, though.'

'What do ya mean?'

'It could all be worse, man. We could be like him. Imagine living in an abandoned pub in Poland and picking cabbage for your living. I mean, who'd give a fuck if he disappeared?'

Ben walked on a few steps before he realised that Mick wasn't following.

'I'm swinging in here, man, gonna hop the wall.'

'You really going to her ma's car?'

'Can't go inside and not worth the walk back. I'll tell her you were asking for her, will I? To ring ya, for a coffee or something.'

'Okay.'

They hugged and Mick kept it going longer than Ben felt comfortable. Ben had his earphones in his hand and was readying himself for the last push into Rush. He broke off first and Mick had that mouth where he looked like he was tasting something and was going to speak but he swallowed it, burped and let his watery eyes open and close a few times. Ben moved away and Mick held out his hand.

'Straight home, yeah?'

'Yeah, straight home.'

Ben felt outflanked, pressed in and alone. The main road was more exposed here, no trees or buildings, just a flat spread of wheat fields that became cliffs and plunged into the sea. He walked for fifty metres, looked back and saw Mick sitting on the wall, the light from his phone shining on his face. When he was out of view, Ben crossed back and took the first right into the estates. Katie's family home was in a maze of semi-detached houses called 'Seaview Rise', a dead end that backed onto the new primary school. He picked up his speed and jogged to the little green across from her house. He sat on the ground beneath a large tree and had a clear view of her door. After five minutes, he saw

Mick arrive and disappear behind the car. Soon after, he watched Katie leave; hooded, sketchy and running up the road with her phone and keys in one hand. The lights flicked twice on the car and Mick's head appeared from the kerb. He jumped up and dove into the back seat. Katie hopped in after him. Ben couldn't watch. He felt his fists tighten and release.

He checked his phone: 2:30 on a Thursday morning. He could taste his bed. He'd go for a jog tomorrow to stave off the guilt after the spliff. He was getting fit again. Mick was right, Ben thought, there was a way out of this place. He picked up a rock. The evening was full and fit to burst, something needed to be emptied. The clouds had cleared and the moon was shining brightly. He was glad now he had his runners on. He walked slowly towards the front of the car and didn't look back.

Float Like a Butterfly. Sting Like a Bee.

I

Ali
　　　seems everywhere these days.
I had such a strange dream last night
　　　　　　(just this last night).
It's still part of me,
　　　fresher than yesterday's snow.
　　　　　I was at home
　　　　　　　　and my Dad was there,
he was really *here*
　　　and I even felt the old familiar
　　　　　tension.
We were driving to a supermarket
　　　and he told me to go in
　　　　　to *get that bread.*
　　　　　　　Your mother said you'd know the one.
I was searching the shelves
　　　when a dark second later,
　　　　　I was on the train with a friend,
we passed bridges at Ringsend—
　　　I could see them through the window,
　　　　　past her head.
I kept repeating,
　　　It would be easier if he were dead
　　　　　because I <u>do</u> remember the removal,
　　　　　　the funeral,
the cremation, but oh…
　　　we haven't scattered his ashes yet.
　　　　　She looked me in the eye
　　　　　and said, *that's it—that's what it is.*
You can't let go till it's done.

II

Last week I read
    The Tao of Muhammad Ali
        in one go, trying to devour it
to fill the void and then,
    on a long, long walk
      in this strange place
      I swear
I saw Dad walking in the field
    walking alongside me a good deal away.
      I remembered that
when I was nine
    he sent me to school with a story to tell
      how before the Liston fight,
        Ali declared that,
The sun ain't gonna shine no more.
    No one laughed
      but I bore their ignorance proudly
        as only a nine year old can
and though later Dad said—
    You rejected everything I loved,
      It was not true.
You see,
    I've been trying to put it all together—
      Dad, Ali, the sudden death
of a neighbour, his seventeen-year-old son
    who is left,
      the robin I saw that morning
        before we got the word,
    so alive
against the grey January fields,
    and then later,
      finding it by the gatepost
        and not wanting to look

/ poem continues

and see the damage
     the car had done because
        it was still a small handful,
          warm,
        and in all this, all that rings true,
    all I have to hold to
is the full moon I saw the other night
           and that line of Tess Gallagher's
             on Carver's last night:
               The moon shone like
the last beat of a mad man's heart.

III

Maybe I'll stick with the story
        of the neighbour—
it seems more manageable
     than my own
       sprawling grief;
my landlady asks if
    I want his old armchair—
      I'd need to see it first,
but she hesitates,
    not wanting me (or anyone)
      to see the state they'd lived in,
or more, that his son might know
    I'd seen.
     She's kept a fire lit
       in case he comes back
from his aunt's and on an impulse says,
      Come on and no one'll see.
     We go in.
She leads me into the grey cottage
     and the cloying smell of damp
        assails us.

In the bedroom,
by the double bed they shared
                    the wallpaper is dark and peeling.
                        They never lit the fire,
she says, *made do with the electric.*
            She's packed the dead man's clothes
                    in black plastic bags,
                            and plans to paint
so when the son comes back
            it'll be a different place,
                        different
to that which he shared with his father
        for eight years.
I look at the chair
        through the bedroom door, decide not to take it.
As I leave something catches my eye,
            the wall is papered with clippings—
                    Evander Holyfield in victory,
                            arms upraised.
The young lad boxes.
        He'd come home and wake his Dad
                if he won.
                    When he'd lose the man would say,
            Sure, even Cassius Clay lost sometimes.
Even Ali?
Even Ali.

Nell Regan

Conversations with Friends
an extract

Sally Rooney

That night Nick and I sat together at dinner. After the food was finished Melissa opened another bottle of wine and Nick leaned over to light my cigarette. When he shook the match out he placed his arm on the back of my chair quite casually. Nobody seemed to notice, actually it probably looked perfectly normal, but I found it impossible to concentrate while he was doing it. The others were talking about refugees. Evelyn kept saying: some of these people have degrees, these are doctors and professors we're talking about. I had noticed before this tendency of people to emphasise the qualifications of refugees. Derek said: whatever about the others, imagine turning doctors away. It's insane.

What does that mean? said Bobbi. Don't let them in unless they've got a medical degree?

Evelyn said that wasn't what Derek meant, and Derek interrupted Evelyn to say something about Western value systems and cultural relativism. Bobbi said that the universal right to asylum was a constituent part of the 'Western value system' if any such thing existed. She did the air quotes.

The naive dream of multiculturalism, Derek said. Žižek is very good on this. Borders do exist for a reason, you know.

You don't know how right you are, said Bobbi. But I bet we disagree about what the reason is.

Nick started laughing then. Melissa just looked away as if she wasn't paying attention to the conversation. I pulled my shoulders back fractionally to feel Nick's arm against my skin.

We're all on the same side here, Derek said. Nick, you're an oppressive white male, you back me up.

I actually agree with Bobbi, said Nick. Oppressive though I certainly am.

Oh, God save us, Derek said. Who needs liberal democracy? Maybe we should just burn down Government Buildings and see where that gets us.

I know you're exaggerating, said Nick, but increasingly it's hard to see why not.

When did you get so radical? Evelyn said. You're spending too much time around college students, they're putting ideas in your head.

Melissa tipped some ash off her cigarette into a tray she was holding in her left hand. She was smiling then, a comical little smile.

Yeah, Nick, you used to love the police state, Melissa said.What happened?

You invited all these college students on holiday with us, he said. I was powerless to resist.

She sat back and looked at him, through the glimmer of smoke. He lifted his arm off the back of my chair and put his cigarette out in the ashtray. The temperature seemed to drop perceptibly, and I saw everything in dimmer colours.

Did you stop by the lake earlier? she said.

On the way back, yeah, said Nick.

Frances got sunburnt, Bobbi said.

Actually I wasn't really burnt, but my face and arms were a little pink, and warm to the touch. I shrugged.

Well, Bobbi insisted on taking her clothes off and getting into the water, I said.

You snitch, said Bobbi. I'm ashamed of you.

Melissa was still looking over at Nick. He didn't seem at all unsettled by this; he looked back at her and smiled, a relaxed and spontaneous smile, which made him look handsome. She shook her head in a gesture of amusement or exasperation, and finally looked away.

We all went to bed late that night, at about two in the morning. For ten or twenty minutes I lay on my bed in the dark hearing the quiet complaint of floorboards above me, and doors clicking shut. No voices. Bobbi's room next door was entirely silent. I sat up and then lay down again. I felt myself developing a plan to go upstairs for a glass of water, though I wasn't really thirsty. I could even hear myself justifying my thirst with reference to the wine I'd had at dinner, as if I would later be subject to interview about what I was doing upstairs. I sat up again, feeling my own forehead, which was normal temperature. Quietly I crept out of bed and up the stairs, wearing my white nightdress with the pattern of tiny rosebuds. The light in the kitchen was on. My heart started to beat very hard.

Inside the kitchen Nick was putting the clean wine glasses away in the cabinet. He looked up at me and said: oh, hello. Instantly, like I was reciting something, I replied: I felt like a glass of water. He made a humorous face, like he didn't really believe me, but he handed me a glass anyway. I poured the water and then stood against the fridge door to drink it. It was lukewarm and tasted chlorinated. Eventually Nick stood in front of me and said, there aren't any more wine glasses, so. We were looking at each other. I told him he was a total embarrassment and he said he was 'extremely aware' of that. He put his hand on my waist and I felt my whole body lift toward him. I touched the buckle of his belt and said: we can sleep together if you want, but you should know I'm only doing it ironically.

Nick's room was on the same floor as the kitchen. It was the only bedroom on that floor of the house; the others were upstairs or else down in the basement like mine. His window was open onto the sea, so he pulled the shutters over quietly and closed it while I got onto the bed. When he was inside me I pressed my face into his shoulder and said: does it feel okay?

I keep wanting to say thank you, he said. That's weird, isn't it?

I told him to say it and he did. Then I told him I was coming and he shut his eyes and said, oh. Afterwards I sat with my back against the wall, looking down at him, where he was lying on his back and breathing.

I've had a rough couple of weeks, he said. I'm sorry about the thing on the internet.

I know I was being cold toward you. I didn't realise you had pneumonia.

He smiled, he touched the soft underside of my knee with his fingers.

I thought you wanted me to leave you alone, he said. I was really sick and lonely, you know. It just seemed like you wanted nothing to do with me.

I thought about saying: no, I wanted you to tell me that you dreamt about me at night.

I was having a bad time too, I said. Let's forget about it.

Well, that's generous. I think I could have handled it a lot better.

But I forgive you, so it's okay now.

He sat up on his elbows then and looked at me.

Yeah, but I mean you've forgiven me very quickly, he said. Considering I tried to break up with you. You could have dragged it out a lot more if you wanted.

No, I just wanted to get back into bed with you.

He laughed, as if this delighted him. He lay back down with his face turned away from the light, his eyes closed.

I didn't think I was that good, he said.

You're okay.

I thought I was a total embarrassment.

You are, but I take pity on you, I said. And the sex is very nice.

He said nothing. I couldn't sleep in his room that night anyway, in case someone saw me leaving in the morning. Instead I went back down to my own bed and lay on my own, curled up as small as I could go.

The next day I felt warm and sleepy, like a child. I ate four slices of bread at breakfast and drank two whole bowls of coffee, with cream and sugar. Bobbi called me a little pig, though she said she meant this 'in a cute way'. And I brushed Nick's leg under the table and watched him trying not to laugh. I was filled with an exuberant, practically spiteful sense of joy.

Three whole days passed this way in Étables. At mealtimes out in the garden, Nick and Bobbi and I sat together at one end of the table and interrupted one another a lot. Nick and I both found Bobbi screamingly funny and we always laughed at everything she said. Once Nick cried at breakfast when Bobbi did an impersonation of a friend of theirs called David. We had only met David briefly, at literary things in Dublin, but Bobbi had his voice down perfectly. Nick also helped us to improve our language skills by speaking to us in French and repeatedly pronouncing the 'r' noise on request. Bobbi told him I could already speak French and that I was faking it to get his lessons. We could see it made him blush, and she flashed her eyes at me across the room.

On the beach in the afternoons, Melissa sat under a parasol reading the newspaper while we lay in the sun and drank from water bottles and reapplied sun lotion on each other's shoulders. Nick liked to go swimming and then come back out of the water glistening wet and looking like an advertisement for cologne. Derek said he found it emasculating. I turned a page in my Robert Fisk book and pretended not to listen. Derek said: Melissa, does he spend a lot of time preening? Melissa didn't look up from her newspaper. She said, no, he's just naturally gorgeous, I'm afraid. That's what you get when you marry for looks. Nick laughed. I turned another page in the book although I hadn't read the previous one.

For two nights in a row, I went to bed on my own until I heard the house go quiet, and then I went up to Nick's room. I didn't feel too tired to stay up late, though during the day I often fell asleep at the beach or in the garden. We couldn't have been getting more than four or five hours' sleep, but he didn't complain of feeling tired, or hurry me out of his room even when it was very late. After the first night, he stopped drinking wine with dinner. I don't think he had anything to drink again at all. Derek pointed this out frequently, and I noticed Melissa offering him wine even after he said he didn't want any.

Once when we were coming up from the sea together after swimming, I asked him: you don't think they know, do you? We were waist deep in the water still. He shielded his eyes with the flat of his hand and looked at me. The others were back on the shore, with the towels, we could see them. In the sunlight my own arms looked lilac-white and dimpled with goosebumps.

No, he said. I don't think so.

They might hear things at night.

I think we're pretty quiet.

It seems insanely risky what we're doing, I said.

Yeah, of course it is. Did that just occur to you now?

I dipped my hands in the water and it stung of salt. I lifted a handful and let it fall back onto the surface from my palm.

Why are you doing it then? I said.

He dropped his hand from his eyes and started to shake his head. He was all white like marble. There was something so austere about the way he looked.

Are you flirting with me? he said.

Come on. Tell me you crave me.

He slapped a handful of water at my bare skin. It splashed my face and felt so cold it almost hurt. I looked up at the spotless blue lid of sky.

Fuck off, he said.

I liked him, but he didn't need to know that.

We smoked a lot that night, and Nick was still kind of high when I got to his room, after everyone else had gone to sleep. He was fully dressed, sitting on the side of his bed and reading something on his MacBook, but he was squinting like he couldn't see the text that well, or it was just confusing. He looked good like that. He was maybe a little sunburnt. I guess I was probably high too. I sat on the floor at his feet and let my head rest against his calf.

Why are you on the floor? he said.

I like it down here.

Oh hey, who was that on the phone earlier?

I closed my eyes and leaned my head harder against him until he said, stop that.

It was my dad on the phone, I said.

He didn't know you were here?

I got up on the bed then and sat behind Nick, with my arms around his waist. I could see what he was reading, it was a long article about the Camp David Accords. I laughed and said, is this what you do when you get high, read essays about the Middle East?

It's interesting, he said. So hey, your dad didn't know you were over here, or what?

I told him, he's just not a very good listener.

I rubbed my nose slightly and then put my forehead on Nick's back, against the white cloth of his T-shirt. He smelled clean, like soap, and also faintly of seawater.

He has some issues with alcohol, I said.

Your dad does? You never told me about that.

He closed his MacBook and looked around at me.

I've never told anyone about it, I said.

Nick sat back against the headboard then and said: what kind of issues?

He just seems to be drunk when he calls me a lot of the time, I said. We've never talked about it in depth or anything. We're not close.

I got into Nick's lap then, so we were facing one another, and he ran his hand over my hair automatically like he thought I was somebody else. He never touched me like that usually. But he was looking at me, so I guess he must have known who I was.

Does your mother know about it? Nick said. I mean, I know they're not together.

I shrugged and said he had always been the same way. I'm a pretty horrible daughter, I said. I never really talk to my dad. But he gives me an allowance when I'm in college, that's bad, isn't it?

Is it? he said. You mean you think you're enabling him, because you take the allowance but you don't hassle him about the drinking.

I looked at Nick and he looked back up at me, with a slightly glassy, earnest expression. I realised he really was being earnest, and he really did mean to touch my hair like that, affectionately. Yeah, I said. I guess so.

But what are you supposed to do instead? he said. The whole financial dependency thing is so fucked up. Everything definitely improved for me when I stopped having to borrow money from my parents.

You like your parents, though. You get along with them.

He laughed and said, oh God, no I don't. Are you kidding? Bear in mind these are the people who made me go on TV when I was ten wearing a fucking blazer and talking about Plato.

Did they make you do that? I said. I assumed it was your idea.

Oh no. I was very troubled at the time. Ask my psychiatrist.

Do you really see a psychiatrist, or is that part of the joke?

He made a noise like hmm, and he touched my hand sort of curiously. He was definitely still high.

No, I have these depressive episodes, he said. I'm on medication and everything.

Really?

Yeah, I was pretty sick for a while last year. And, uh. I had a bad week or two over in Edinburgh, with the pneumonia and all that. This is probably a very uninteresting thing to tell you about. But I'm feeling okay now anyway.

It's not uninteresting, I said.

I knew Bobbi would know what to say in this situation, because she had a lot of opinions about mental health in public discourse. Out loud I said: Bobbi thinks depression is a humane response to the conditions of late capitalism. That made him smile. I asked him if he wanted to talk about being sick and he said no, not desperately. He had his fingers in my hair, at the back of my neck, and his touch made me want to be quiet.

For a little while we kissed and didn't talk at all, except occasionally I would say something like: I want it so much. He was breathing hard then and saying things like hm, and oh, good, like he always did. He put his hand under my dress and stroked the inside of my thigh. I held his wrist on a sudden impulse and he looked at me. Is this what you want? I said. He looked confused, like I was posing a riddle which I might answer for him if he couldn't. Well, yeah, he said. Is it… what you want? I could feel my mouth tightening, the grinding machinery of my own jaw.

You know, sometimes you don't seem that enthusiastic, I said.

He laughed, which wasn't really the sympathetic response I expected. He looked down, his face was a little flushed. Do I not? he said.

I felt hurt then, and said: I mean, I talk a lot about how much I want you and how much fun I'm having and it's never really reciprocal. I feel like I don't fulfil you a lot of the time.

He lifted his hand and started rubbing the back of his neck. Oh, he said. Okay. Well, I'm sorry.

I am trying, you know. If there are things I'm doing wrong I want you to tell me.

In a slightly pained voice he said: you're not doing anything wrong. It's me, you know, I'm just awkward.

That was all he said. I didn't really know what to add, and anyway it seemed clear that no matter how unsubtly I fished for his reassurance he wasn't going to provide it. We went on kissing and I tried not to think about it. He asked if I wanted to get on my hands and knees this time and I said sure. We undressed without watching each other. I put my face in the mattress and felt him touch my hair. He put his arm around my body and said: come here for a second. I knelt upright, I could feel his chest against my back, and when I turned my head his mouth touched the rim of my ear. Frances, I want you so badly, he said. I closed my eyes. The words seemed to go past my mind, like they went straight into my body and stayed there. When I spoke, my voice sounded low and sultry. Will you die if you can't have me? I said. And he said: yes.

When he was inside me, I felt as though I had forgotten how to breathe. He had his hands around my waist. I kept asking him to do it harder, although it hurt a little when he did. He said things like, are you sure that doesn't hurt? I told him I wanted it to hurt, but I don't know whether I really did. And all Nick said was, okay. After a while it felt so good that I couldn't see clearly any more, and I wasn't sure if I could pronounce whole sentences. I kept saying, please, please, though I didn't know what I was asking him for. He held a finger to my lips as if to tell me to be quiet and I took it into my mouth, until he touched the back of my throat. I heard him say oh, no, don't. But it was already too late, he came. He was sweating, and he kept saying: fuck, I'm so sorry. Fuck. I was shivering badly. I felt that I had no understanding of what was happening between us.

By then it had started getting light outside and I had to leave. Nick sat up watching me put my dress back on. I didn't know what to say to him. We looked at one another with agonised expressions and then looked away. Downstairs in my room I couldn't sleep. I sat on my bed, holding my knees against my chest and watching the light move through the chink in the shutters. Eventually I opened up the window and looked out at the sea. It was dawn, and the sky was silvery blue and exquisite. In the room above I could hear Nick walking around. If I closed my eyes I felt that I was very close to him, close enough to hear him breathing. I sat at the window that way until I heard doors opening upstairs, and the dog barking, and the coffee machine switched on for breakfast.

STINGING FLY PATRONS

Many thanks to:

Mark Armstrong
Maria Behan
Trish Byrne
Edmond Condon
Evelyn Conlon
Sheila Crowley
Kristina K. Deffenbacher
Gerry Dukes
Edel Fairclough
Michael J. Farrell
Ciara Ferguson
Olivia Gaynor-Long
Brendan Hackett
James Hanley
Christine Dwyer Hickey
Dennis Houlihan
Peggy Hughes
Nuala Jackson
Geoffrey Keating
Jack Keenan
Jerry Kelleher
Jack Kelleher
Conor Kennedy
Joe Lawlor
Irene Rose Ledger
Róisín McDermott
Petra McDonough
Lynn Mc Grane
Jon McGregor

John McInerney
Finbar McLoughlin
Maggie McLoughlin
Ama, Grace & Fraoch MacSweeney
Mary MacSweeney
Paddy & Moira MacSweeney
Anil Malhotra
Gerry Marmion
Ivan Mulcahy
Mary O'Donnell
Kieran O'Shea
Lucy Perrem
Maria Pierce
Peter J. Pitkin
Mark Richards
Orna Ross
Fiona Ruff
Alf Scott
Ann Seery
Eileen Sheridan
Arthur Shirran
Alfie & Savannah Stephenson
Olive Towey
Debbi Voisey
Ruth Webster
Grahame Williams
Hotel Doolin
Lilliput Press
Tramp Press

*We'd also like to thank those individuals who have expressed the preference
to remain anonymous.*

By making an annual contribution of 75 euro, patrons provide us
with vital support and encouragement.

BECOME A PATRON ONLINE AT STINGINGFLY.ORG

or send a cheque or postal order to:
The Stinging Fly, PO Box 6016, Dublin 1.

NOTES ON CONTRIBUTORS

Tess Barry was shortlisted for the 2015 Manchester Poetry Prize. Twice a finalist for *North American Review*'s James Hearst Poetry Prize and *Aesthetica Magazine*'s Poetry Award, she also was shortlisted for the 2014 Bridport Poetry Prize. Her poems have been widely published. She teaches literature and creative writing at Robert Morris University in Pittsburgh, Pennsylvania. tessbarrypoet.com

Amanda Bell's *Undercurrents* (2016) placed second in the HSA Merit Book Awards and joint second for a Touchstone Distinguished Book Award. Her children's book, *The Lost Library Book*, is published by The Onslaught Press, and her debut poetry collection, *First the Feathers*, will be published this October by Doire Press.

Lorcán Black is an Irish poet, now living in London. His work has been published or is forthcoming in *Fjord's Review*, *Blue Lyra Review*, *Apogee*, *Assaracus*, *The Flexible Persona* and *The Chiron Review*, amongst numerous others. He is founder and Editor in Chief of *Anomaly Literary Journal*.

Dylan Brennan writes poetry and prose. Currently based in Mexico City, his most recent publication is *GUADALUPE & other hallucinations* (The Penny Dreadful Press, 2017), a collection of short prose chronicles accompanied by linocut images made by Belfast-based artist Jonathan Brennan. @DylanJBrennan

Kevin Cahill was born in Cork and graduated from University College Cork with a degree in Government Studies. He has completed his first volume of poems and is seeking a publisher. To date his poems have appeared in *Edinburgh Review*, *The London Magazine*, *Agenda*, *Poetry Ireland Review* and *The Oxonian Review*.

Jill Crawford is a Northern Irish actress and writer. She is about to start an MA in Creative Writing at UEA, and is a graduate of Oxford University. A novel is in progress, supported by the Arts Council of Northern Ireland.

Patrick Deeley is from Loughrea, County Galway. His work has been published widely. The latest of his six collections with Dedalus Press is *Groundswell: New and Selected Poems*. His memoir, *The Hurley Maker's Son*, recently appeared from Transworld Ireland.

Jennifer Down was born in 1990. Her debut novel, *Our Magic Hour*, was published by Text Publishing in early 2016. Her collection of stories, *Pulse Points*, will appear in August 2017. She lives in Melbourne.

Maryanne Doyle is a poet and computer scientist from Dublin who began to share her poetry in late 2015 after writing for ten years. She was recently a finalist in the All Ireland Poetry Slam, performed at Lingo, and for six thousand students at the Cycle Against Suicide's Student Leaders Congress.

Katherine Duffy's second collection, *Sorrow's Egg*, was published by Dedalus Press in 2011. Recent work has appeared in *Magma*, *Orbis*, *The Rialto* and *The Lonely Crowd*. She also writes fiction, in both English and Irish, and won the Hennessy Award in 2006. www.kateduv.com

Molia Dumbleton's work has been awarded the Seán Ó Faoláin Story Prize, the Dromineer Literary Festival Flash Fiction Award, and the Columbia Journal Winter Fiction Award; and featured in literary journals including *New England Review* and *The Kenyon Review* online.

Wendy Erskine lives in Belfast. She has a forthcoming debut collection with The Stinging Fly Press.

Emer Fallon's work has been published in *The SHOp*, *Poetry Ireland Review*, *The Poetry Bus*, and *The Irish Times*. Shortlistings include the Bridport Prize, Listowel Writers' Week, and Fish Poetry Prize. She lives in West Kerry with her family.

Sharon Flynn lives near the Causeway Coast. She fits reading and writing poetry into the corners of her life when she can escape from other commitments. She is currently completing an MA at the Seamus Heaney Centre at Queen's University, Belfast.

Anne Hayden is from Cork and lives in Dublin. Her short fiction has been published in *The Incubator* and *The Irish Times* where she was shortlisted for a 2017 Hennessy Literary Award.

Jo Holmwood is based in County Leitrim. In 2016 she received a highly commended award from the Bridport Prize and was shortlisted for the Bristol Short Story Prize. She also writes plays, which she has directed and produced for audiences in Dublin, Galway and Leitrim.

Synne Johnsson is a Norwegian writer, currently studying creative writing and journalism at Kingston University. She is inspired by the Norwegian author Knut Hamsun and Frank O'Hara. Her work has appeared in Kingston University's student anthology, *Ripple*.

Tess Jolly won the Hamish Canham Prize in 2015 and is this year's winner of the Anne Born Prize. Her debut pamphlet, *Touchpapers*, is published by Eyewear and a sequence of poems, *The Blue Hours*, is forthcoming from Indigo Dreams.

Jill Jones' most recent works include *The Beautiful Anxiety*, which won the 2015 Victorian Premier's Literary Award for Poetry, *Breaking the Days*, which won the 2014 Whitmore Press Award, and a chapbook, *The Leaves Are My Sisters*.

Louise Kennedy's stories have featured in *Ambit*, *Wasifiri* and *The Incubator* and on *Arena* on RTÉ Radio 1. Prizes include Listowel-Los Gatos, Short Fiction Journal and John O'Connor in 2016. She grew up in Holywood, County Down, and lives in Sligo.

Pippa Little lives in Northumberland and is a Royal Literary Fellow at Newcastle University. Her second full collection, *Twist*, was published in April 2017 by Arc.

Aoife Lyall is an Irish poet living in the Scottish Highlands. Shortlisted for both the Hennessy New Writing Awards and the Patrician Press Poetry Prize in 2016, she is currently writing her first collection.

Is as Árainn Mhór i dTír Chonaill do **Phroinsias Mac a' Bhaird**. Scríobhann sé idir fhilíocht, phrós agus dhrámaíocht agus tá 10 leabhar i gcló aige, trí chnuasach filíochta ina measc.

Paul McCarrick's poetry has featured in *Boyne Berries*, *Skylight 47*, *wordlegs*, and placed third in the 2015 Over The Edge New Writer Competition. His novel, *Happy-Cry with my Brilliant Life*, was longlisted at the 2014 IWC Novel Fair.

Afric McGlinchey is a freelance editor living in West Cork. Her first collection, *The Lucky Star of Hidden Things*, was recently published in Italian by L'Arcolaio. Her second collection, *Ghost of the Fisher Cat*, was published by Salmon Poetry in 2016. africmcglinchey.com

Eamon Mc Guinness is from Dublin. His writing has appeared in *Looking at the Stars*, *Abridged*, *The Honest Ulsterman*, *The Bohemyth*, *Skylight 47*, *Bare Hands Poetry* and *The Galway Review*. He is on the Strokestown International Poetry Prize shortlist 2017. He holds an MA in Creative Writing from UCD.

Lisa McInerney's work has featured in *Winter Papers*, *The Stinging Fly*, *Granta* and on BBC Radio 4. Her debut novel *The Glorious Heresies* won the Baileys Women's Prize for Fiction and the Desmond Elliott Prize. *The Blood Miracles*, her second novel, was published in April 2017.

Geraldine Mitchell's third collection, *Mountains for Breakfast*, was published by Arlen House in March 2017. A former Patrick Kavanagh Award winner, her two previous collections are *World Without Maps* (Arlen House, 2011) and *Of Birds and Bones* (Arlen House, 2014).

K. S. Moore's poetry has recently appeared in *The Ogham Stone* and *Crannóg*. Poems have also featured in *Ink Sweat and Tears, And Other Poems* and *Nutshells and Nuggets*. Flash fiction and short stories have been published in *FlashFlood, Metazen, Number Eleven* and *The Bohemyth*.

David Murphy's poetry has been published many times in magazines and anthologies in Ireland and abroad, including *The Burning Bush, Cyphers* and *The SHOp*. Also a short story writer and novelist, his latest book is a fiction-memoir called *Walking on Ripples* (Liffey Press, 2014). davidmurph.wordpress.com

Doireann Ní Ghríofa is a bilingual writer working both in Irish and English. Among her awards are the Rooney Prize for Irish Literature, the Michael Hartnett Prize, and the Ireland Chair of Poetry bursary. Her most recent book is *Oighear* (Coiscéim, 2017).

Michael Nolan is 26 years old, from Belfast. His work has been published by *Salt* and *The Stinging Fly*. He is the fiction editor of *The Tangerine*, and is currently studying for a PhD in Creative Writing at Queen's University, Belfast.

Philip Ó Ceallaigh has published over forty stories, many of them collected in *Notes from a Turkish Whorehouse* and *The Pleasant Light of Day*, published by Penguin. He was awarded the Rooney Prize in 2006. His work has been translated into eleven languages. He lives in Bucharest, Romania, and sometimes in a tent in a clearing in a forest in Bulgaria.

Aidan O'Donoghue was born in 1980. His fiction has previously appeared in *The Los Angeles Review, The Stinging Fly*, and *The Tangerine*. He is currently working on a poetry collection and a short-story collection. He lives in Cork.

Aiden O'Reilly's short-story collection, *Greetings, Hero,* was published in 2014. He lived for nine years in Eastern Europe and is now based mainly in Dublin. He graduated in mathematics, and has worked as translator, building-site worker, mathematics lecturer, and property magazine copywriter.

Colm O'Shea is from Leixlip, County Kildare. A winner of the Irish Writers Centre Novel Fair in 2012, his short fiction has appeared in *gorse, The Bohemyth, 3AM Magazine, Visual Verse* and *Hotel*.

Stephanie Papa is a poet and translator living Paris, France. She has an MFA degree in Poetry from the Pan European programme. She is poetry co-editor of *Paris Lit Up*. Her work has been published in *World Literature Today, Niche, Yasakmeyve, NOON, great weather for media, Four Chambers Press, Paris/Atlantic, Literary Bohemian, Rumpus,* and more. She organises writing workshops and readings in Paris

Nora Pyne lives in Dublin. This is her second story published in *The Stinigng Fly*.

Nell Regan's latest poetry collection is *One Still Thing*, Enitharmon Press and she is a recent Patrick and Katherine Kavanagh Fellow. Her biography *Helena Molony: A Radical Life 1883-1967* has just been published by Arlen House.

Emer Rogers lives in Dublin. This is her first published short story.

Sally Rooney was born in Mayo. Her writing has appeared in *The Stinging Fly*, *The Dublin Review*, *Granta* and *Winter Pages*. Her first novel, *Conversations With Friends*, is published by Faber & Faber in June 2017.

Susanne Stich is originally from Nürnberg, living in the Northwest of Ireland. Her short stories have appeared in *Ambit*, *The Incubator*, *The Impressment Gang*, and many other literary magazines. She is also a regular contributor to *The Honest Ulsterman*.

Anne Tannam's first collection *Take This Life* (WordOnTheStreet) was published in 2011 and her second collection *Tides Shifting Across My Sitting Room Floor* (Salmon Poetry) is forthcoming in May 2017. Also a spoken word poet, she has performed at Electric Picnic and Lingo.

Nathan Thanki is a human ecologist and jack-of-all-trades climate justice activist currently based in Belfast but often found wandering further afield. He likes whiskey and R&B, sometimes together.

Jessica Traynor's first collection, *Liffey Swim* (Dedalus Press), was shortlisted for the 2015 Strong/Shine Award. Awards include the Ireland Chair of Poetry bursary 2014, the Hennessy New Writer of the Year Award 2013 and the Listowel Single Poem Award 2011. Poems are featured or forthcoming in *The Deep Heart's Core* (Dedalus), *Acumen*, *Rochford Street Review*, *Prelude* and *Poetry Ireland Review* among others.

NOTE ON THE COVER

by Gavin Corbett

Declan, the editor of this magazine, asked me, in my capacity as writer-in-residence at Temple Bar Gallery + Studios, to select the cover images for the next couple of issues from the works of the artists in studio. For this issue, I picked a piece by Stephen Dunne, *Here Come the Brittle Men*. The image is dynamic without being queasily busy, and the colour range is narrow and the tones are nice and solid, so it makes for a punchy and readable picture. There's something mesmeric about the repeated but slightly varied faces and costumes. It reminds me of the folks who frequent Grogan's pub in Dublin—frayed, theatrical, dissolute, a mix of the self-aware and the completely oblivious—and the threat of murder that bubbles up from between the street setts as soon as the patrons stagger out of its doors. Here's what Stephen himself has to say about it:

> 'It's a picture of drunken camaraderie, but perhaps they're drunk on power. They might be pirates or redcoats. A colonial hangover. (Or they could just be dressed up.) There's an element of the ridiculous about their costume—the stupid hats, peacocks. They're anachronistic like the process of making the image itself. The laughter is important; it's both slapstick and uneasy: What have they just done, what are they about to do? The laughing cavalier by Frans Hals is in there somewhere, but crowded out, swarmed. I'm interested in trapping a certain kind of spontaneity in the work so it was painted all in one go over a few hours, without references or copying, so it maintains a fluidity, each character running into the next like a stack of cards. They fall like skittles. Their masculinity is brittle, caught up in violence and domination. The red ink is like stains, overly intense, just like the picture's subjects. A warning.'

Gavin Corbett's second novel, *This Is The Way*, was named 2013 Kerry Group Irish Novel of the Year and shortlisted for the Encore Award. His latest novel, *Green Glowing Skull*, was published in 2015.